THIRD EDITION

THE PAST TODAY

Complete Junior Certificate History

SKILLS & RESOURCES

Dermot Lucey

GILL EDUCATION

Gill Education
Hume Avenue
Park West
Dublin 12
www.gilleducation.ie

Gill Education is an imprint of M.H. Gill & Co.

978 07171 6521 6

Original design by Lyn Davies, setting by Carole Lynch

The paper used in this book is made from the wood pulp of managed forests. For every tree felled, at least one tree is planted, thereby renewing natural resources.

Contents

Introduction iv

YEAR 1 HOW WE FIND OUT ABOUT THE PAST

1 The Job of the Historian 1
2 The Work of the Archaeologist 6
3 The Mesolithic Period (Middle Stone Age) 11
4 The Neolithic Period (New Stone Age) 14
5 The Bronze Age 17
6 The Iron Age and the Celts 19
7 Early Christian Ireland 23
8 Ancient Rome 29
9 Medieval Society: Castle, Church and City 33
10 The Renaissance 38

YEAR 2 STUDIES OF CHANGE

11 The Age of Exploration 42
12 The Reformation 50
13 Plantations in Ireland 57
14 The American War of Independence 61
15 The French Revolution 64
16 Ireland in the Age of Revolutions 66
17 From Farm to Factory 70
18 Special Study – Contrasting Lifestyles *c.* 1850: Industrial England and Rural Ireland 73
19 Special Study – Rural Ireland in the 1840s 76

YEAR 3 Understanding the Modern World

20 Towards an Independent Ireland, 1900–22 81

21 The New State 88

22 Northern Ireland: From Foundation to Attempts at Peace, 1920–85 101

23 Social Change in 20th-Century Ireland 108

24 Part 1: Peace and War in Europe, 1920–45 117

25 Part 2: The Rise of the Superpowers, 1945–91 135

26 Part 3: Moves towards European Unity 137

27 Part 4: Asian Nationalism after 1945 – Gandhi and Indian Independence 138

Active History 139

Introduction

Welcome to the new ***The Past Today Skills & Resources*** book – leading a new student-centred approach to History. It reflects the changing focus of assessment strategies with an emphasis on key skills and assessment.

An invaluable companion to ***The Past Today***, ***The Past Today Skills & Resources*** tracks the **Junior Certificate syllabus** through ***The Past Today*** textbook chapter by chapter. It fosters **literacy**, **numeracy**, **source analysis** and other **historical** skills by the imaginative use of documents, pictures, statistics, graphs and charts. It includes hundreds of **up-to-date questions** which promote active learning, enhance skills and reinforce knowledge.

Key ideas at the start of each topic are ideal for **easy revision** and **Focus Tasks** develop **research skills** and deepen understanding of historical events. Throughout, it promotes the idea of the student as an historian. It provides the ideal **skills & resources book** and **exam-trainer** that can be used in class or for homework.

The Past Today has helped thousands of students across the country to understand and engage with History. Now completely updated, ***The Past Today***, together with its companion ***The Past Today Skills & Resources***, will continue to help students to achieve their maximum potential through enjoyable, active and effective learning. We hope you enjoy it!

Dermot Lucey

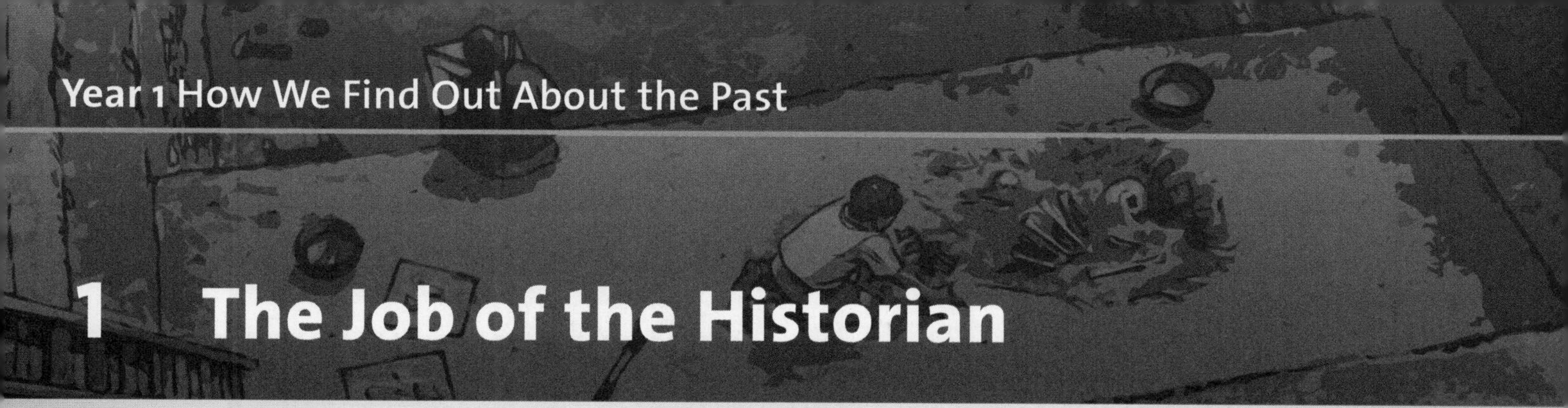

Year 1 How We Find Out About the Past

1 The Job of the Historian

Key ideas

History – the story of the past, using sources.

Sources – evidence used by historians to investigate the past: written (newspapers), non-written (buildings, objects), visual (photographs), oral (interviews).

Archive – for documents, e.g. National Archives; museum – for objects (artefacts), e.g. National Museum.

Primary source – source from the time which is being studied, e.g. a newspaper, first-hand account.

Secondary source – source from after the time that is being studied, e.g. *The Past Today*.

Bias – one-sided account; propaganda – using information to promote your view; sources accurate and reliable, advantages and disadvantages.

Chronology – putting events in order of time – decade, century, age/era, BC, AD.

Skills of the historian – locate information (research), sort information, understand causes, ask questions, make judgments and communicate ideas; facts and opinions.

1 Select the words from the list below and insert them in the correct boxes.

Word List: Primary; Secondary; Letters; Oral; Artefacts; Written; Biography; Evidence; Buildings; Photographs; Ruins; Newspapers; Job; Interview; Documentary.

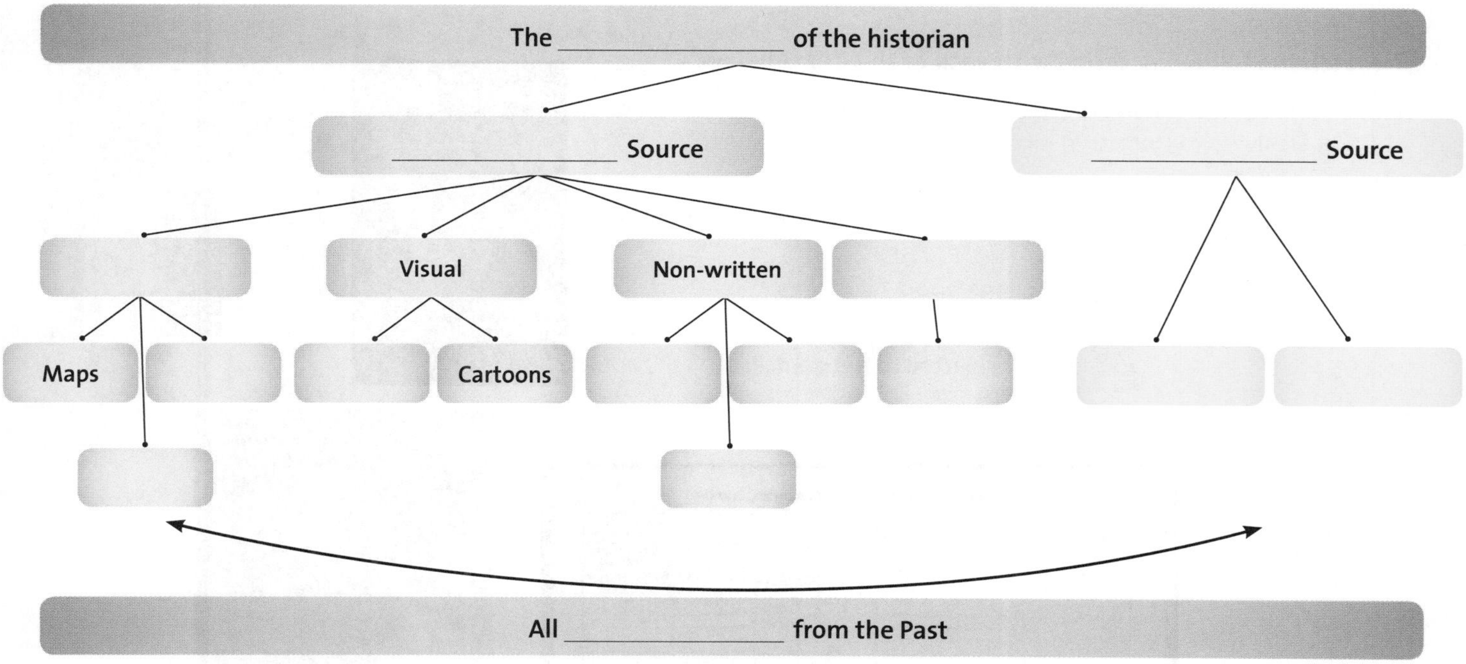

❷ Match each Key Term with the corresponding explanation. ☆ Literacy

1	History	A	One hundred years
2	Archive	B	A manmade object
3	Opinion	C	Putting events in order of time
4	Propaganda	D	Where documents are stored
5	Artefact	E	A personal view of what happened
6	Century	F	Using information to influence a person
7	Chronology	G	The story of the past based on evidence

1	
2	
3	
4	
5	
6	
7	

❸ Explain each of the following terms used by **historians**. ☆ Literacy

Fact	
Bias	
Museum	
Census	
Decade	
BC	
AD	

❹ Match the following terms with each of the items below. ☆ Historical skills

(1) chronology; (2) fact; (3) opinion; (4) propaganda; (5) archive; (6) artefact; (7) monument.

1	
2	
3	
4	
5	
6	
7	

A He is the greatest rugby player of all-time.

B 1984, 1992, 2000

C She was elected to the council.

D

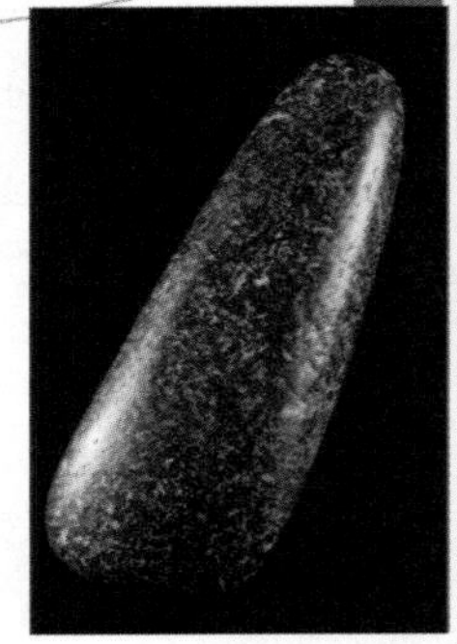

E

F

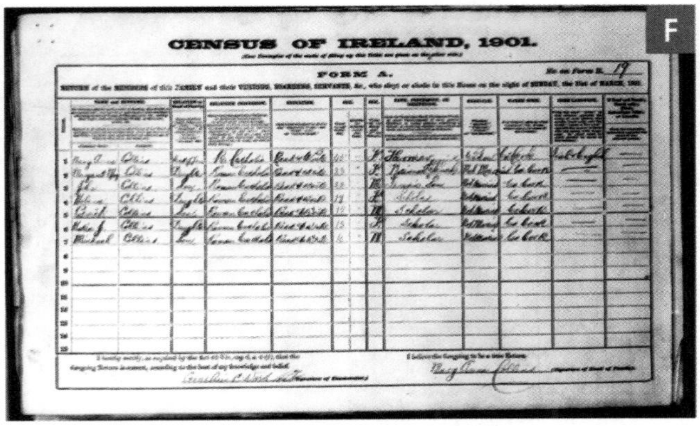

CENSUS OF IRELAND, 1901.

FORM A.

G

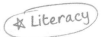

5 (a) If you were researching the history of the 1916 Easter Rising, which of the following sources could you use from the list below? (Please tick)

(b) Which of the sources you have chosen are primary (P) and which are secondary (S)?

Sources	✔	P or S
Irish Independent, Wednesday, 26 April, 1916		
Enda Delaney, *The Great Irish Famine, A History in Four Lives*, Gill & Macmillan, Dublin, 2014		
The 1916 Rising: Personalities and Perspectives, an online exhibition, www.nli.ie/1916/		
A photograph of Fairyhouse Race Course on Monday, 24 April, 1916		
A diary of an Irish soldier fighting in the First World War		
The Diary of Anne Frank		
The GPO, Dublin		
Pádraig Yeates, *A City in Wartime, Dublin 1914–1918*, Gill & Macmillan, Dublin, 2012		

6 Study these photographs of Mussolini, who was dictator of Italy from 1922 to 1943, and the document accompanying them.

SOURCE ANALYSIS: PICTURES & DOCUMENTS

(i) What differences do you notice between the two photographs (Documents A and B)?

(ii) Which of the two photographs has been changed, A or B? Explain your answer by referring to information in Document C.

DOCUMENT A

DOCUMENT B

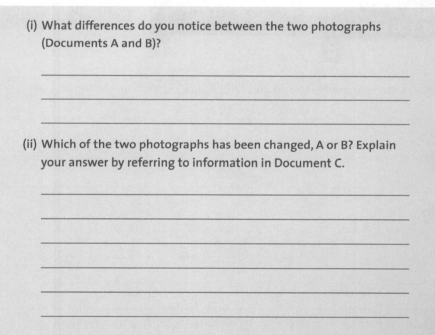

DOCUMENT C

A factor in Mussolini's favour was his enormous talent for self-advertisement. He exploited his journalistic talents to the full, not only convincing many Italians that 'Mussolini is always right', but creating an image, far from the truth, of a man who possessed all the talents. The controlled press portrayed him as an excellent violinist, fine horseman, daring pilot, bold war hero, and as an intellectual who had mastered all the major philosophies of the day.

(*Source:* Adapted from T. Morris, D. Murphy, *Europe 1870–1991*, Collins Educational, London, 2000)

7 **Propaganda:** Study these posters on recruiting in Ireland during World War I and answer the questions below.

SOURCE ANALYSIS: PICTURE

A

B

C

D

E

(i) What features (symbols, views, colours, etc.) are used in the posters to convince men to join the British army?

(ii) Why are these features used in these posters?

(iii) Which posters appeal to
- (a) Fear
- (b) Pride
- (c) Shame
- (d) Any other emotion?

(iv) Select two of the posters; how effective is each of the posters you have chosen in getting its message across?

(v) What have you learnt about how propaganda works?

❽ **Insert the following information in the timeline below.** ✯ Chronology

BC; AD; → The present day; 77 BC; Year 1; 2nd century AD; 2nd century BC; AD 140; 277 BC

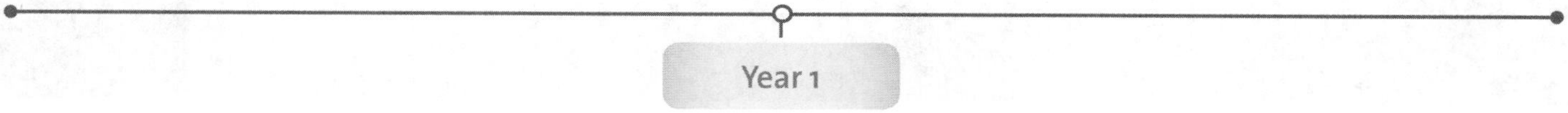

❾ Focus Task (in groups of two or three) ✯ Research skills SOURCE ANALYSIS ✯ Group work

Using the internet, access **two conflicting newspaper stories** about a major recent world event. What are the differences in the stories? Why do the stories differ, do you think? What did you learn about bias and propaganda from the stories? Explain your answers by using information from both newspaper reports.

(i) The topic

(ii) The newspapers

(iii) The differences

(iv) Why do the stories differ, do you think?

(v) Examples of bias and/or propaganda

(vi) What did you learn about bias and propaganda from these stories?

2 The Work of the Archaeologist

Key ideas

Archaeology – the story of the past from material remains.

Artefacts – objects made by people, e.g. spears, coins.

Prehistory – the history of people before writing was invented.

Finding sites – above ground, below ground: chance discoveries, stories from history, aerial photography, geophysical survey, underwater evidence.

Excavation or dig – survey, grid of squares, shovels, trowels, brushes, sieves, numbered, clipboard, ranging rod, catalogue, photograph, drawing, laboratory.

Dating – stratigraphy, coins and pottery, tree-ring dating (dendrochronology), radiocarbon dating, bones, plants.

Conservation – protecting and preserving; tourism, many historical attractions.

1 Match the Key Term with the corresponding explanation. Literacy

1	Archaeology	A	A manmade object
2	Artefact	B	Grains from plants
3	Prehistory	C	Layers in the ground
4	Excavation	D	Where objects are stored
5	Museum	E	Before writing
6	Stratigraphy	F	The story of the past from material remains
7	Pollen	G	Systematic digging of the ground to find archaeological evidence

1	
2	
3	
4	
5	
6	
7	

2 Explain each of the following terms used by **archaeologists**. Literacy

Salvage or rescue archaeology	
Crop marks	
Aerial photography	
Geophysical survey	
Tree-ring dating	
Radiocarbon dating	
Conservation	

❸ Match the following terms with each of the items below. ✯ Literacy

(1) clearing topsoil; (2) recording findings on a laptop; (3) trowel; (4) stratigraphy; (5) sketching; (6) ranging rod; (7) artefact.

1	
2	
3	
4	
5	
6	
7	

A

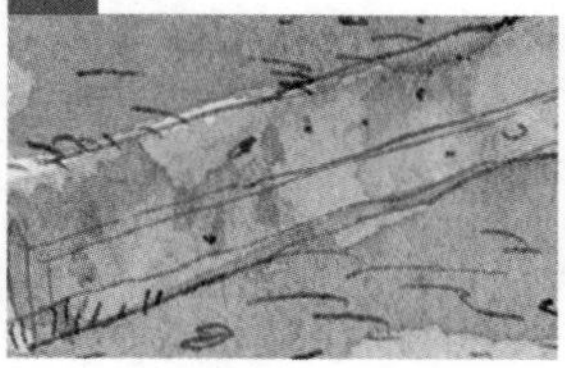

B

C

D

E

F

G

❹ **Source Analysis and Archaeological Methods:** the case of Heinrich Schliemann and the Siege of Troy. ✯ Research skills

SOURCE ANALYSIS: DOCUMENTS

(A) Please read Document A and answer the questions on the next page.

DOCUMENT A

Heinrich Schliemann was a 19th-century German banker, obsessed with the myth of the Trojan War. He was desperate to find the ancient city of Troy where, according to the blind poet Homer, Hector, Odysseus and Achilles were locked in battle over 3,000 years ago. In 1869 Schliemann discovered a little hill called Hissarlik in Turkey. He believed that underneath it was the city he was looking for. Unfortunately, in his desperation to justify his theory, he dug through layer after layer of archaeology until he found it. The site became famous. Mrs Schliemann's photograph was published in all the world's newspapers dressed in jewellery they thought might once have adorned the fair face of Helen of Troy.

But in fact Schliemann hadn't found Homer's Troy at all. Within three years of his death his theory was disproved by one of his co-workers. The jewellery and the site were authentic, but from a completely different period. Vast amounts of irreplaceable archaeology had been destroyed in the pursuit of a dream, and Hissarlik now looks like a bombsite. Some archaeologists say it's the worst case of deliberate archaeological vandalism they've ever seen. Good archaeology is about observing and recording what's actually there, not searching for something and then persuading yourself that the evidence fits your theory.

(*Source*: Robinson & Aston, *Archaeology is Rubbish*, Channel 4 Books, 2003, p. 100)

(i) What did Heinrich Schliemann believe he had discovered in 1869?

(ii) What artefacts did Schliemann find during his excavations at Hissarlik in Turkey?

(iii) What discovery did Schliemann's co-worker make?

(iv) Give **two** reasons why Schliemann's dig has been criticised by archaeologists.

(v) What is your view of the work of Schliemann, as stated in Document A? Explain your answer.

(vi) Name **two** methods of dating which an archaeologist would use to date objects found on a site.

(B) Read Document B and answer the questions that follow. **Optional**

DOCUMENT B

The contemporary history of the site and its subsequent exploration and conservation dates from 1793, when it was discovered. It was identified by scholars, first as Ilion in 1810 and then as Troy in 1820. Heinrich Schliemann first visited the site in 1868. Between then and his death in 1890 he carried out seven major campaigns, completed in 1893–94 by his assistant, Wilhelm Dörpfeld. It was in 1873 that he found the famous gold hoard, known erroneously as 'King Priam's Treasure', as it came from Troy II, not Troy VIIA. Excavations over more than a century have revealed 23 sections of the defensive walls around the citadel, eleven gates, a paved stone ramp, and the lower portions of five defensive bastions. These date for the most part from Troy II and VI; however, a section of the earliest wall (Troy I) survives near the south gate of the first defences. The great residential complex from Troy II consists of five parallel long buildings with porches (*megara*). The largest of these is considered to represent the prototype of the Greek temple. The ensemble is considered to have constituted some form of palace. The remains of a number of long rectangular houses from Troy II are to be seen at the bottom of one of the most striking features off the site, the so-called Schliemann Trench, dug by the famous 19th-century excavator in search of the 'Citadel of Priam', the object of his search.

(*Source: Archaeological Site of Troy*, whc.unesco.org/en/list/849)

(i) Do Documents A and B agree or disagree? Explain your answer.

(ii) After reading Document B, do you agree with the opinion you gave in A(v) above?

____

____

(C) Do further research on the work of Heinrich Schliemann. For example, you could read the entry on Heinrich Schliemann in Wikipedia, especially the section under Criticisms.

(i) What is your view of the three accounts of the work of Schliemann (Documents A, B and Wikipedia)?

____

____

(ii) What did you learn about archaeological methods?

____

____

(iii) What did you learn about analysing documents?

____

____

5 Construct a bar graph using the following information on visitors to historic sites in Ireland in 2012. ☆ Numeracy

1	Book of Kells	561,259
2	National Museum, Kildare St, Dublin	409,275
3	St Patrick's Cathedral, Dublin	385,000
4	Kilmainham Gaol	310,910
5	Bunratty Castle and Folk Park	286,270

(*Source*: Fáilte Ireland)

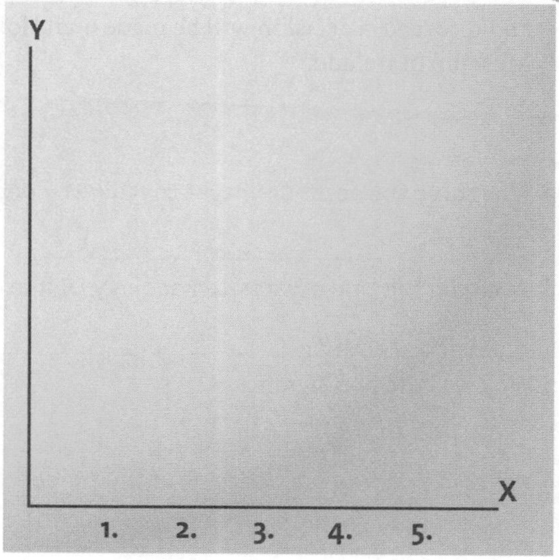

6 Use www.chartgo.com to construct the same graph.

Which is more useful for historians – a bar graph or a column of figures, such as the above?

____

____

7

SOURCE ANALYSIS: DOCUMENT

Ancient oak structure from Connemara coast excavated and taken into State care

Archaeologists believe trackway may be preserved fulacht fiadh or ancient cooking place

The north Connemara coastline could be one of this island's richest 'time capsules' of life before sea levels rose, according to State archaeologists who have removed a 3,700-year-old structure from the shore in Co. Galway. A team from the Underwater Archaeology Unit has excavated the entire oak structure, resembling an ancient trackway, which was exposed on the coastline at Lippa near Spiddal by last winter's storms.

The 'trackway', discovered earlier this spring, may in fact be a very well-preserved and highly significant example of a fulacht fiadh, or ancient cooking place, constructed at a time when forests and lagoons extended out into what is now Galway Bay. The timbers could be part of a wooden trough which was encircled by 17 hazel rod stakes, according to the unit's head, Finbarr Moore.

'It is very significant, as it is unusual to find a fulacht fiadh at such a level of preservation, but the sea obviously conserved it when levels began to rise,' he said. 'While thousands of fulacht fiadh have been recorded and excavated during road-building schemes, most of them are stone-lined and have a mound of burnt stone nearby. We found no firecracked stones near this structure, but the wattle surround could be unique.'

Preservation in situ of the archaeological material was 'not a realistic option', as the timbers were not fastened to any underlying structure and would not have survived another period of storms, he said.

Radiocarbon analysis undertaken by local community activist Seán Ó Coistealbha dated it to 1,700 BC.

The Department of Arts, Heritage and the Gaeltacht said: 'Once the excavated material is fully analysed and recorded, a decision will be made on its long-term conservation, in consultation with the National Museum of Ireland.'

(*Source*: Lorna Siggins, *Irish Times*, 19 August 2014)

(i) Why could the north Connacht coastline be one of Ireland's 'richest "time capsules"'?

(ii) What did the Underwater Archaeology Unit excavate?

(iii) Why was the find significant?

(iv) How did they work out the age of the timber?

(v) Why was the timber preserved for so long?

(vi) 'A decision will be made on its long-term conservation.' What do you think should happen to the find?

3 The Mesolithic Period (Middle Stone Age)

Key ideas

Stone Age – stone tools and weapons – axes, spear, scrapers, harpoons; artefacts.

Mesolithic – Middle Stone Age; first people in Ireland; circular huts; saplings; hearth; along lakes, rivers, coasts.

Hunter-gatherers – hunted animals, gathered berries; fished – dugout canoes; spears; harpoons; fish traps on rivers.

Nomadic – moved to other locations to find food.

Cooking spit – for cooking food; middens – waste heaps or pits.

Flintstone – stone used in weapons and tools – stone axe; arrowheads; microliths – small flint pieces.

Scrapers – stone to clean skins.

Burials – cremated bodies; buried burnt bones; Mount Sandel, Co. Derry; Lough Boora, Co. Offaly – evidence of mesolithic sites; carbon dating; post-holes.

1 Explain each of the following terms relating to the **Mesolithic Period**. ☆ Literacy

Stone Age	
Dugout canoe	
Post-holes	
Hunter-gatherer	
Middens	
Microliths	
Nomadic	
Harpoon	
Scraper	

2 Match the following terms with each of the items below.

(1) flint scraper; (2) needle; (3) microlith; (4) axe head; (5) cooking spit; (6) shaping flint.

1	
2	
3	
4	
5	
6	

A

B

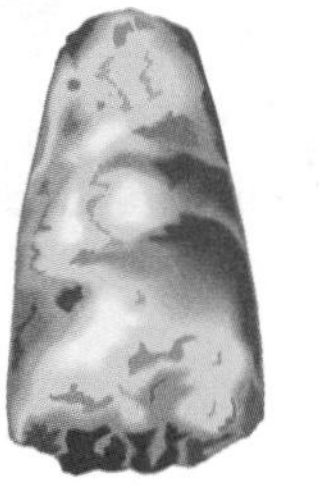

C

D

E

F

3

SOURCE ANALYSIS: DOCUMENT

The Mesolithic site at Mount Sandel was excavated during the 1970s by Peter Woodman of University College Cork. Woodman found evidence of up to seven structures, at least four of which may represent rebuildings. Six of the structures are circular huts of six meters (about nineteen feet) across, with a central interior hearth. The seventh structure is smaller, only three meters in diameter (about six feet), with an exterior hearth. The huts were made of bent sapling, inserted into the ground in a circle, and then covered over. Radiocarbon dates at the site indicate that Mount Sandel is among the earliest human occupations in Ireland, first occupied around 7000 BC.

(*Source*: K. Kris Hirst, www.archaeology.about.com/od/mesolithicarchaic/a/mount_sandel.htm)

Lough Boora Mesolithic site was discovered by a local man from Kilcormac digging on the east edge of the lake in 1977. This discovery was investigated, and what was thought at first to be a stone roadway was actually a storm beach on the shore of what had been an enormous Ice Age lake. Scattered along it were the charcoal heaps of hearths tended by hunter-gatherers some 9,000 years ago – only about 1,000 years after the glaciers retreated, a remnant of an era when the Shannon and its lakes – Lough Ree and Lough Derg – covered much more of the midlands than today. It is one of the most important archaeological finds in Ireland. Prior to its discovery it was thought that the first human settlements were near to the coast and that the midlands remained uncolonised. The discovery of the Lough Boora Mesolithic site has proven this to be inaccurate and pushed the accepted date for the colonisation of the midlands back by over 3,000 years!

(*Source*: www.offalytourism.com)

The excavations at Ferriter's Cove were begun by renowned Irish archaeologist, Professor Peter Woodman and his team in 1983, after a local amateur archaeologist discovered a Stone Age flint knife. When Woodman began his excavations, Ferriter's Cove was believed to be a Neolithic (late Stone Age) site.

The results of Woodman's excavations showed that Ferriter's Cove was inhabited during the Mesolithic (middle Stone Age) period. In fact, carbon dating indicated that the mudstone axes found there were from around 4350 BC. This was a hugely important discovery, because previously archaeologists had thought that Ireland was largely uninhabited during the Mesolithic period, apart from a small area in the east.

(*Source*: www.chooseireland.com/kerry/ferriters-cove)

What do the documents tell you about Mesolithic Ireland that you did not know already? Discuss three key points.

4 The Neolithic Period (New Stone Age)

Key ideas

First farmers – grew crops, domesticated animals, cleared forests, fields; mattock, wooden plough, wheat, barley, dairying; changed landscape.

Houses – wattle and daub, timber planks, thatched roof, hearth, permanent settlement.

Food – grain, saddle stone, fished, hunted, gathered berries, animal skins, woollen clothes, spinning and weaving.

Tools and weapons – polished stone axes, mainly from Co. Antrim, knives, scrapers, arrows, bone and antler needles, jewellery.

Pottery – clay coils; cooking, storing food, burials.

Burial customs – building megalithic tombs, court cairns, portal dolmens, passage graves, corbelled roof, winter solstice, cremation, burial chambers, afterlife.

Neolithic sites – Lough Gur, Co. Limerick; Céide Fields, Co. Mayo; Newgrange, Co. Meath; pollen analysis; carbon dating.

1 Classify each of the following as **similarities or differences** between the Mesolithic Period and the Neolithic Period.

Historical skills

spears · hunting · weaving · arrows · nomadic · carbon dating · wattle and daub · cooking spit · plough · middens · stone tools · farming · fields · Mount Sandel · Lough Gur · polished stone axes · dugout canoes · permanent · cremation · megalithic tombs · pottery · spinning · gathering · stratigraphy · passage graves · mattock · saddle stone · fishing

Similarities	Differences

2 Read the account below and answer the questions that follow.

SOURCE ANALYSIS: DOCUMENTS

Seeing the Light as Solstice Hits the Net

It was new age technology combined with 5,000-year-old Stone-Age engineering. Yesterday, for the first time, the winter sun lighting the passage tomb at Newgrange, Co. Meath, was beamed live around the world on television and the internet.

Hundreds of people travelled long distances to face the sun as it rose over the Boyne Valley, as locals had done thousands of years earlier. The morning frost may have chilled fingers, but it provided perfect crisp weather for viewing the winter solstice. Witnessed by just a select few inside the snug burial chamber, the annual event was transmitted live by the Office of Public Works to hundreds of thousands of people via internet and television stations, including TV3.

It was 40 years ago that Helen Watanabe-O'Kelly first witnessed the event alongside her father, Professor Michael J O'Kelly, who rediscovered the winter solstice phenomenon when he unearthed the roof box. Yesterday saw his daughters – Helen, Eve and Ann – return to the chamber as part of the select group of dignitaries and lottery winners to celebrate the 40th anniversary of Professor O'Kelly's remarkable discovery.

'It was extraordinary, I remember seeing it in around 1969 – all alone, just me and him. No cameras, no lights, nothing. The whole place was just illuminated. I'll never forget it,' Ms Watanabe-O'Kelly said. 'He was the first person in about 5,000 years to see it.'

Outside, incense burned as some watchers saluted the rising sun, others simply watched while the sun set the roof box aglow. On a massive screen outside the passage tomb, from just before 9 am the beam of amber light could be seen creeping along the floor.

(*Source*: Louise Hogan, *Irish Independent*, 22 December 2007; www.newgrange.com/winter_solstice.htm)

(i) What was 'new age technology'?

____

(ii) What was 'Stone-Age engineering'?

____

(iii) How were they combined?

____

(iv) What event was transmitted on TV and the internet?

____

(v) Who organised the transmission?

____

(vi) Who rediscovered the winter solstice phenomenon?

____

(vii) What is the winter solstice phenomenon?

____

____

(viii) What time of the day did this happen?

____

3 Match words in Column A with the corresponding items in Column B. (☆ Literacy)

Column A		Column B	
1	Pollen analysis	A	Court cairn
2	Boyne Valley	B	Gathering
3	Farming	C	Artwork
4	Hearth	D	Carrowmore
5	Neolithic house	E	Portal dolmen
6	Scythe	F	Changed landscape
7	Hazelnuts	G	Plant growth & changes
8	Jewellery	H	Cooking spit
9	Saddle stone	I	Ulster History Park
10	Tievebullagh	J	Grinding corn
11	Corbelled roof	K	Beads
12	Capstone	L	Stone axes
13	Newgrange	M	Cutting corn
14	Spirals, circles	N	Neolithic site

1	
2	
3	
4	
5	
6	
7	
8	
9	
10	
11	
12	
13	
14	

4 Focus Task (☆ IT)

Use Google Earth to find each of the following places relating to Neolithic Ireland. Write one statement about what you find there. Use street view and photographs if they are available.

Poulnabrone Dolmen, Co. Clare

Dún Aengus, Aran Islands

Newgrange, Co. Meath

Céide Fields, Co. Mayo

5 The Bronze Age

Key ideas

Bronze Age – first use of metal.

Bronze – a mixture of copper and tin, smelted in a furnace; use of moulds; Mount Gabriel, Killarney (copper), Cornwall (tin).

Houses – wattle and daub; thatched roof; timber fence.

Work – *Farming:* wooden spades; ploughs; bronze sickle; cattle, sheep, pigs, grain. *Cooking:* cooking spits; bronze cauldrons; chopping wood; grinding corn; saddle stone.

Fulachta Fiadh – ancient cooking places; wet, low-lying places; cooked meat.

Ornaments – lunulae, sun discs, torcs, necklaces, bracelets.

Burial – cist graves, wedge tombs; grave goods, urns, bodies burned/cremated.

Standing stones – in a circle, in a row, on their own; for religious ceremonies or burials.

1. Match the terms in Column A with the corresponding items in Column B. Literacy

Column A		Column B	
1	Wattle and daub	A	Arrowheads, beads, pins
2	Cauldron	B	Co. Wicklow
3	Fulacht fiadh	C	Cutting corn
4	Gold	D	Cooking pot
5	Wedge tomb	E	Shapes for weapons and tools
6	Moulds	F	Interwoven sticks covered by mud
7	Sickle	G	Method of cooking
8	Grave goods	H	Cremation

1	
2	
3	
4	
5	
6	
7	
8	

2. Identify each of the following items or activities.

A

B

C

D
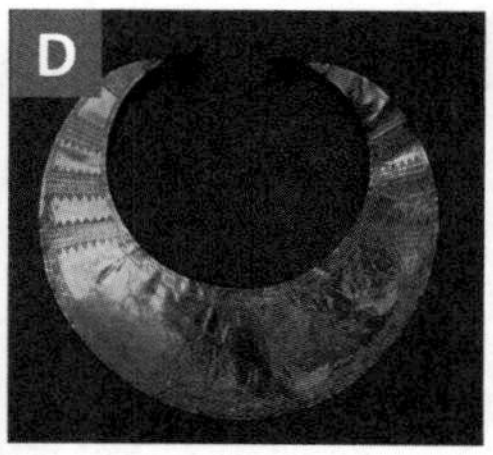

E

F

G

H

I

A	
B	
C	
D	
E	
F	
G	
H	
I	

❸ Writing a People in History answer. (✯ Communication)
Write about the person below. If you wish, you may use the hints to help you in your answer. Write the title at the top of the account.

(i) A person in Ireland during the Bronze Age

Hints are given in Ordinary Level People in History questions, but not in Higher Level questions

Hints: Housing; clothing and food; farming methods; arts and crafts; burial customs

Writing the answer

Begin with a sentence stating who you are e.g. I am a person living in Ireland during the Bronze Age. Say some more about who you are e.g. a farmer. Then write about where you live e.g. housing. Use historical information in your answer e.g. wattle and daub walls; thatched roof; hearth; circular; cooking spit; timber or wattle fence; outhouses; fields; farming methods; surrounding countryside. Mention where other people live. Then go on to clothing and food; arts and crafts; and burials. Use historical information or terms to fill out your answer. Make a list of those terms for each heading. Now you are ready to write.

8–10 significant historical statements

6 The Iron Age and the Celts

Key ideas

Settlements – ring-forts, crannógs, hill-forts, promontory forts.

Ring-forts – circular shape with houses, for farmers.

Crannógs – artificial lake dwellings.

Hill-forts – larger than ring-forts, built on hills, ceremonies; promontory forts – built on headlands or cliffs, ceremonies; souterrains – underground passages or tunnels in ring-forts.

Rí – king; warriors and Aos Dána – people with special skills, e.g. judges, druids (priests), filí (poets), craftsmen; farmers rented land; labourers and slaves did most of the work.

Women – cooking, spinning, rearing children.

Food – cattle, sheep, pigs; milk, butter, cheese; grain: rotary quern – to grind grain.

Cooking – spits, fulachta fiadh.

Tools and weapons – made of iron; ornaments – of bronze and gold; art style – La Tène – spirals, curved lines, florals.

Burials – cist graves, plain graves, grave goods, bog bodies: ogham stones – standing stones with ogham writing.

1 History proved wrong – Castle debate says 'nay' to Celts

SOURCE ANALYSIS: DOCUMENT

An enthralled audience which filled the Parade Tower to capacity heard four of Ireland's leading Celtic scholars defend and attack the motion, 'The Celts – did they occupy Ireland?'

The question was debated on two levels. The negative, if the Celts did not come to Ireland, then how and why do we have a Celtic language which is a reality. This strong argument was advanced by Professor David Stifter, professor of Old Irish in Maynooth College, who was supported in this contention by Dr Graham Isaac of NUI Galway. There seemed little opportunity to set aside the logic and rational of their well argued position.

Indeed, with faint praise Professor Tadhg O'Keeffe acknowledged their argument was cogent, well argued and substantial. That was before he in a stroke dismissed it with the remark, 'What a pity it is also so wrong!' Calling on his undoubted expertise in the world of archaeology he alluded to the total absence of any Celtic structures, the total absence of finds of any artefacts of a nature which could be linked to the Celtic race. He sited the extent of arrowheads, spears, ritual monuments, standing stones, barrows, stone circles and ring forts all of which date to the Bronze Age prior to the supposed arrival of the Celts in 500 BC. The total absence of any artefacts linked to the style which has become known as the Hallstatt and dating to 700 BC to 400 BC he suggested should remind all that not one item of this type or period has ever been found in Ireland. 'Not one,' he declaimed. The Hallstatt period gets its name from a small town in Austria, site of a burial ground of this period. The term has become associated with an early cultural phase of the late Bronze Age/early Iron Age in Europe. Despite the telling effect of a pithy remark from a lady in the audience, 'The absence of evidence is not evidence of absence', by the force of his arguments – together with his personality – he succeeded in turning the scales among the audience and, with Professor Peter Woodman, Professor Emeritus of Archaeology in UCC, the 'nays' won the day.

The debate organised by Kilkenny Archaeological Society proved a most entertaining and informative evening. At the end of the evening only 29 people from the 124 in attendance remained convinced that the Celts did occupy Ireland.

(*Source*: Adapted from www.kilkennypeople.ie, 14 April 2012)

(i) What was the motion of the debate?

____

(ii) What was the main argument in favour of the Celts occupying Ireland?

____

____

(iii) What were the arguments against the Celts occupying Ireland?

____

____

(iv) Which side of the debate won?

____

2 Explain each of the following Key Terms in relation to **Celtic Ireland.** ☆ Literacy

Aos Dána	
Brehon	
Crannóg	
Derbhfine	
Druid	
Filí	
Tuath	

3 Match the following terms in relation to the **Iron Age and the Celts** with each of the items below. ☆ Literacy

(1) ogham; (2) promontory fort; (3) ring fort; (4) souterrain; (5) torc (6) hill fort.

1	
2	
3	
4	
5	
6	

4 Circle the **5 incorrect words** in the passage below and insert the correct words in the box on the side.

Historical analysis | Literacy

Celtic Ireland was divided into about 100 kingdoms. Each kingdom, or conntae, was ruled by a king (banrion). The king was elected from the royal family, or *derbhfine*. He had to lead and protect the tribe. Below the king were nobles, commoners and slaves. Among the nobles were farmers and the *Aos Dána*. The *Aos Dána* included commoners.

1	
2	
3	
4	
5	

5 **Writing a People in History answer.** Communication

Write about the person below. If you wish, you may use the hints to help you in your answer. Write the title at the top of the account.

Hints are given in Ordinary level People in History questions, but not in Higher level questions

(i) A person in Ireland during the Iron Age

Hints: housing; clothing and food; farming methods; arts and crafts; burial customs.

Writing the answer

Begin with a sentence stating who you are, e.g. I am a person living in Ireland during the Iron Age. Say some more about who you are, e.g. a farmer, a warrior, a king. Then write about where you live, e.g. housing. Use historical information in your answer, e.g. ring fort; earthen banks; circular; ditch; timber or wattle fence; wattle and daub walls; thatched roof; hearth; outhouses; souterrain. Mention where other people live. Then go on to clothing and food; farming methods; arts and crafts; and burials. Use historical information or terms to fill out your answer. Make a list of those terms for each heading. Now you are ready to write.

8–10 significant historical statements

___

___

___

___

___

___

___

___

___

___

___

___

6 Scientific Analysis

These are some of the analyses (investigations) that were carried out as part of the Bog Bodies research. Select any three of them and explain what scientists might learn from each of the analyses.

(i) Pollen analysis (ii) Dietary analysis (iii) Dermatological analysis (iv) Dental analysis (v) Gut and stomach contents analysis (vi) CT scanning (vii) MRI scanning.

7 Focus Task – Google Earth

Use Google Earth and Street View to find the following landmarks or features of Celtic Ireland: describe what you find.

Staigue Fort, Co. Kerry, 51.8053°N; 10.0158°W

Hill of Tara, Co. Meath, 53.5775°N; 6.6119°W

Crannóg, Craggaunowen, Co. Clare, 52.8116°N, 8.7930°W

How useful is Google Earth for investigating landmarks from Celtic Ireland?

7 Early Christian Ireland

Key ideas

St Patrick – missionary sent by Pope to convert Ireland to Christianity; end of Celtic religion and the druids.

Early monasteries – founded to honour God, to pray.

Founders of monasteries – St Enda (Aran Islands), St Finian (Clonard), St Brendan (Clonfert), St Íte (Killeedy, Co. Limerick).

Centres of learning – Bible studied, manuscripts copied, metalworking; strict rules; long tunics; location – on important routes or in remote places, e.g. Clonmacnoise, Glendalough, Clonard, Kells, Skellig Michael.

Buildings – church, refectory, monks' huts/cells, scriptorium, cemetery.

Round towers – bell towers, storage, safety, prestige, e.g. Glendalough, Clonmacnoise.

Manuscripts – hand-written books, copies of gospels, lives of saints, e.g. Cathach, Book of Durrow, Book of Kells; materials – vellum (calfskin), parchment (sheepskin), quills, ink.

Metalworking – chalices, croziers, brooches, filigree, e.g. Ardagh Chalice, Derrynaflan Chalice; book shrines to protect manuscripts.

High Crosses – scenes from Bible; Muireadach's Cross.

Irish monks abroad – St Columcille – Iona; St Columbanus – Continent.

1. Match the following terms relating to **Early Christian Ireland** with the definitions. (Literacy)

(1) filigree; (2) high cross; (3) oratory; (4) refectory; (5) scribe; (6) scriptorium.

A	Where manuscripts were copied	
B	Where monks ate their meals	
C	Gold wire on chalices	
D	Carved from stone with scenes from the Bible	
E	A copier of manuscripts	
F	A church	

2. Explain each of the following terms relating to **Early Christian Ireland**. (Literacy)

Book of Kells	
Cathach	
Parchment	
Vellum	
Manuscript	
Round tower	

❸ Chronological sorting (★ Numeracy)

Put the following statements about Ireland from the Stone Age to Early Christian Ireland in chronological order. Insert the numbers in the correct chronological order in the box on the right.

1 Hill forts were built on a prominent site on a hill.
2 Bronze Age people were mostly farmers who cleared trees to use the land for farming.
3 Around 4000 BC, new people came to Ireland. They came by boat – dugout canoes or skin-covered boats. These people were Ireland's first farmers.
4 Burial places have also been found with stone circles, stone rows and standing stones.
5 Neolithic houses were usually rectangular in shape.
6 The main work of the people was providing food through hunting and fishing.
7 Round towers were built in some monasteries, such as Glendalough and Clonmacnoise.

Earliest

❹ The reliability of manuscripts

SOURCE ANALYSIS: DOCUMENTS

Irish scribes were sometimes commissioned (given the job) by families and churches to write political documents. These documents were propaganda texts to create links from one family to earlier powerful ancestors or saints. In doing so, a family's status could increase by virtue of these ancestors.

One hundred years after Brian Boru's death, his great-grandson, Muircherrach, commissioned a text entitled 'The war of the Irish with the foreigners' (Cogadh Gaedhel re Gaillibh). While the author drew on existing records of annual events (the annals), he also incorporated a largely fictional account of the battle (of Clontarf). He mythologised (created myths about) Brian Boru and made him into a saintly, heroic and partly legendary figure. Later writers and artists wrongly treated the text as historical truth, adding a mythical dimension to an already successful king of Ireland.

(*Source*: Dublinia Heritage Centre)

(i) Why were scribes asked by families and churches to write political documents?

____

(ii) How long after Brian Boru's death was 'The war of the Irish with the foreigner' written?

____

(iii) What propaganda did the scribe use in his account?

____

(iv) What dangers is the author of this display board warning historians about?

____

____

5 Monasteries in early Christian Ireland

Number each of the following monasteries in the accompanying map: (1) Clonmacnoise (2) Glendalough (3) Skellig Michael (4) Clonard (5) Kells (6) Clonfert (7) Monasterboise (8) Derrynaflan.

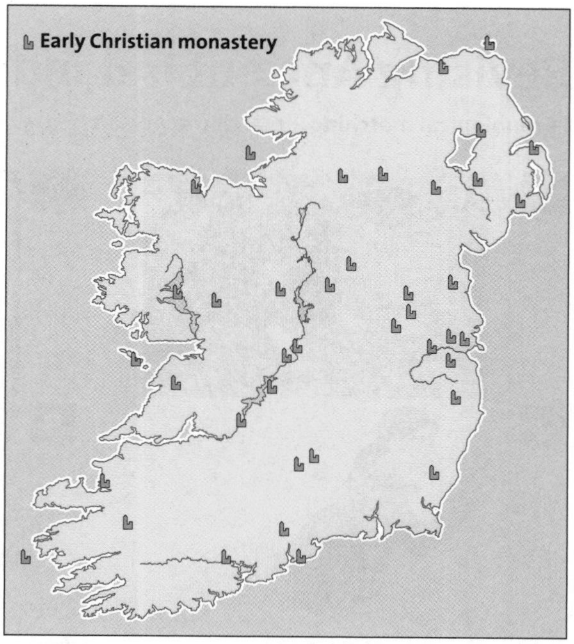

What is the name of the early Christian Irish monastery nearest to you?

____

6 Monastic Art

Identify each of the following examples of monastic art.

1	
2	
3	
4	
5	
6	

1
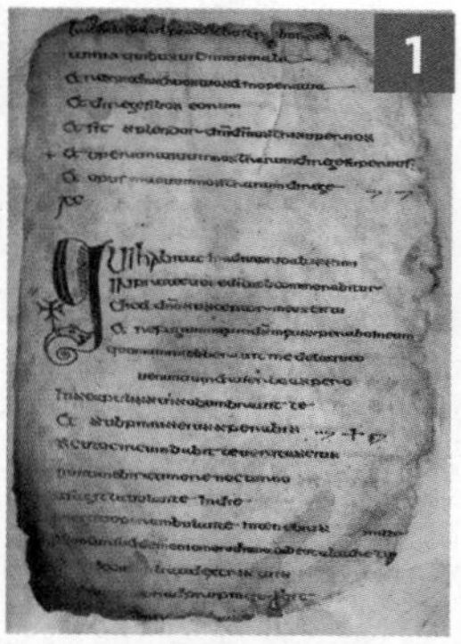

2

3

4

5

6

7 Focus Task

Archaeological monuments near you

(IT) (Research skills)

Investigate the National Monuments Service Archaeological Survey database at http://webgis.archaeology.ie/NationalMonuments/FlexViewer/
Insert your county name and the name of your townland or town, and search.

How many archaeological monuments are listed in your locality? ______________________________

How many of those monuments are from ancient Ireland? ______________________________

What is the oldest monument listed near you? ______________________________

Revising Ancient Ireland

Chronological matching – match the person (1–7) with the feature (A–G), and insert the age or period with each one

1

A
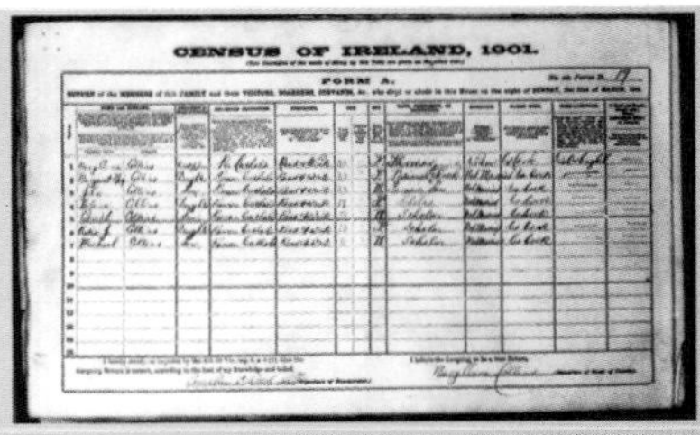
CENSUS OF IRELAND, 1901.
FORM A.

2

B

3

C

4

D

5

E

6

F

7

G

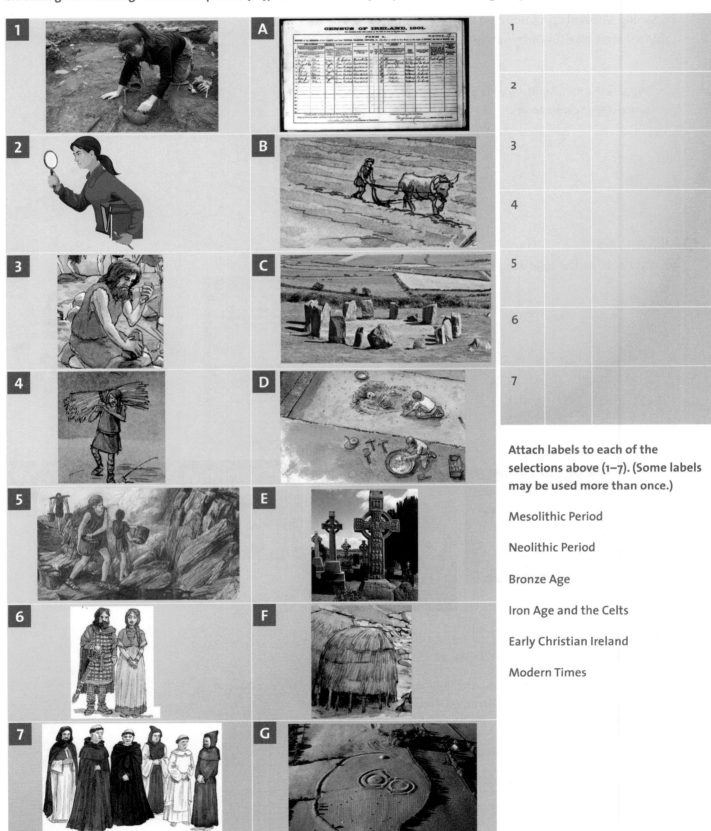

1		
2		
3		
4		
5		
6		
7		

Attach labels to each of the selections above (1–7). (Some labels may be used more than once.)

Mesolithic Period

Neolithic Period

Bronze Age

Iron Age and the Celts

Early Christian Ireland

Modern Times

SOURCE ANALYSIS: DOCUMENTS

10,000-year-old settlement unearthed in Cork

The earliest known settlers in Co. Cork were hunter-gatherers who lived near Fermoy more than 10,100 years ago. That's according to archaeologists who will reveal a wealth of information about our ancestors when they launch a book published by the National Roads Authority on Dec 10 at UCC.

It details illustrated accounts of the 114 significant excavations undertaken in the county, revealing a wealth of previously unrecorded sites, each adding to our understanding of the story of Cork – going back to the county's first known settlers, more than 500 generations ago.

While the 8100 BC settlement in Fermoy, uncovered during the construction of the M8, is deemed to be the oldest, evidence of similarly ancient hunter-gatherers was discovered near Ballincollig and Youghal. Houses built by Cork's first farmers (c.3900 BC) were found near Ballincollig and Fermoy, while a substantial Bronze Age settlement was found near Rathcormac.

The most exceptional discovery was the Mitchelstown Face Cup, dating to the Bronze Age.

'This is the oldest known three-dimensional representation of a person ever discovered in Ireland,' said Mr Hanley, NRA project archaeologist. 'It was radio carbon-dated to 1800 BC. It is unique. It came as a complete surprise. It was a spectacular find.'

A sauna dating to 1400 BC was uncovered at Scartbarry, near Watergrasshill.

The NRA has funded more than 2,000 excavations on national road projects since it was established in 1994.

(*Source*: Sean O'Riordan, *Irish Examiner*, 2 December, 2013)

(i) How many excavations were undertaken in Co. Cork by the National Roads Authority (NRA)? ______

(ii) Why were these excavations undertaken?

______

(iii) What term or word is used to describe the archaeology undertaken by the NRA?

______

(iv) Where was the oldest settlement discovered?

______

(v) Construct a simple timeline of Ancient Ireland and mark in the discoveries/finds mentioned here along the timeline.

(vi) Is the source above a primary source or a secondary source? Explain your answer.

______

______

Revising Ancient Ireland

Literacy

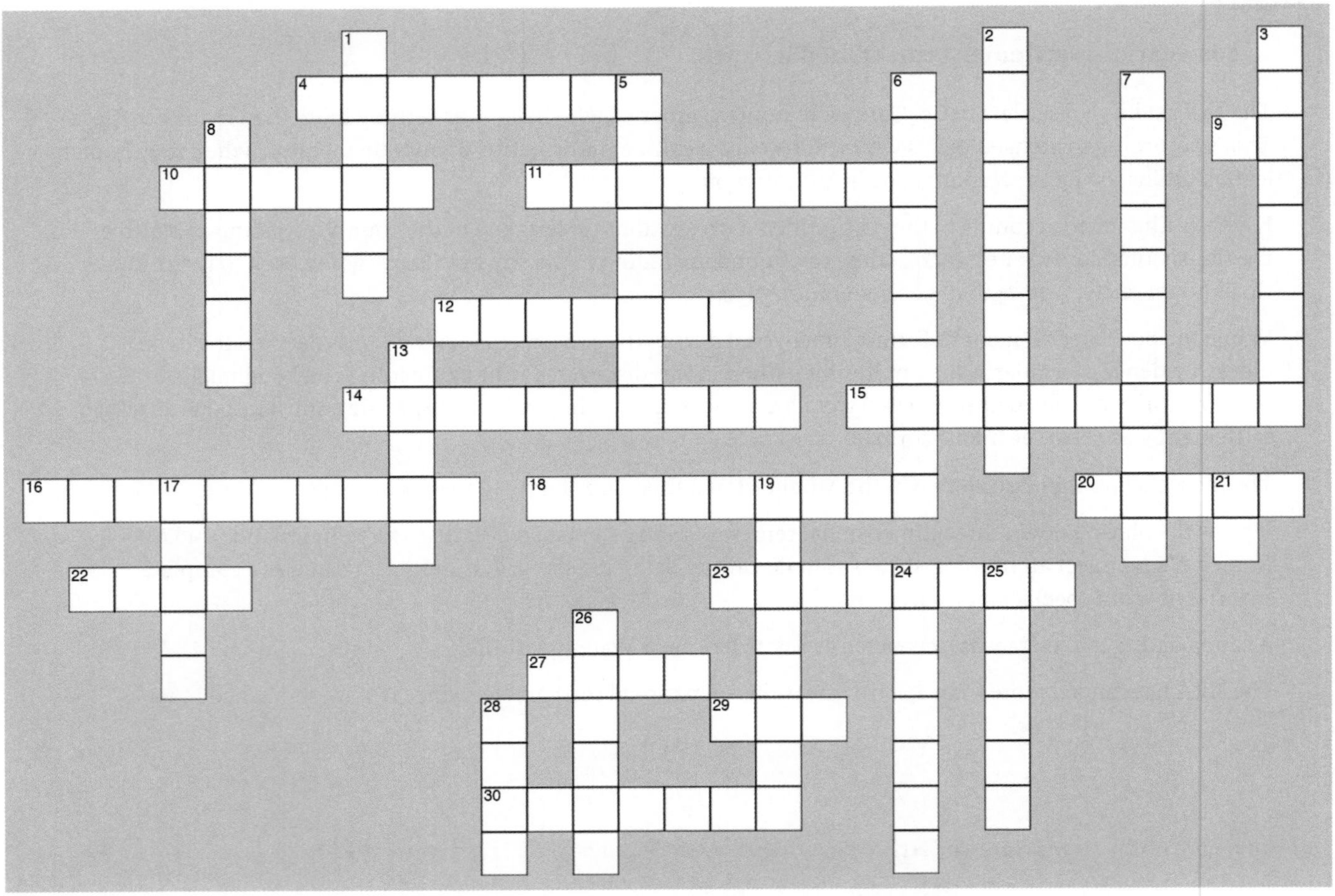

ACROSS

4 Celtic festival.
9 Before the birth of Christ.
10 Waste heap or pit, often of shells.
11 Berries and nuts.
12 First-hand account.
14 Before written documents.
15 Ordering in time.
16 Passage under a ringfort.
18 First farmers in Ireland.
20 Earliest writing in Ireland.
22 One-sided account.
23 Locate information.
27 Neck ring or ornaments.
29 Part of bronze.
30 Lake-dwelling.

DOWN

1 Storing objects.
2 Digging for archaelogical finds.
3 Source from after the events.
5 Man-made object.
6 First people in Ireland.
7 The past from material remains.
8 Tool for cutting corn.
13 One of the Aos Dana.
17 Celtic territory ruled by a king.
19 Dating objects.
21 After the birth of Christ.
24 Storing documents.
25 Part of bronze.
26 Big stones at door of tomb.
28 Something that definitely happened.

8 Ancient Rome

Key ideas

Roman Empire – North Africa, Turkey, Mediterranean Sea as far north as Hadrian's Wall.

Roman towns – forum, grid pattern, amphitheatre (Colosseum), public baths, aqueducts, theatre, circus (stadium) – (Circus Maximus), walls, gates.

Houses – *domus* (private), patricians, plebians, atrium, *peristylium* (garden), mosaics, murals, frescoes, villas, *insulae* (apartments), shops at ground level.

Family – father (head), mother (household); tunic, toga, stola; wheat, porridge, dole, cena for rich people; education, primary, secondary for boys only; arranged marriage.

Entertainment – gladiators, Colosseum, 50,000 people, slaves, criminals, nets, trident, shields, swords, helmets, chariot racing, Circus Maximus (four teams), 250,000, plays, theatres, public baths (hot, cold, warm), strigil.

Work – farming, villa, cereals, craftsmen, work for government, soldiers, legionnaires, centurion, weapons, slaves.

Art and architecture – classical, columns, rounded arches, domes, concrete, aqueducts, sculpture, copied Greek style, frescoes (wet plaster).

Burials – gods (Jupiter, Neptune), goddesses (Juno, Venus), life after death, River Styx, Charon, coin, procession, tombs, cremation, death masks, Christians, burials, catacombs, Constantine.

Decline and legacy – decline: civil wars, barbarians, cost of army; legacy: towns and cities (London, Paris); language – influence of Latin; architecture, sculpture, Renaissance; calendar; Christianity; laws.

1 **Archaeological Evidence**

These items were found in a Roman rubbish pit. Study the source and answer the questions on the next page.

(i) What types of food were eaten by this family?

____

(ii) What evidence was found to show how the food was cooked?

____

____

(iii) What evidence would you use to date this pit?

____

____

(iv) How would you know that this pit was in the house of a well-off family? Use the following headings in your answer: Evidence from food; Evidence from other objects found in the rubbish pit.

____

____

____

____

(v) How do we know there were children in the family?

____

____

(vi) What other items would you have expected to find in a pit like this?

____

____

2 Match the following terms relating to **Ancient Rome** with the definitions. (Literacy)

1	Amphitheatre	A	Women's clothes
2	Aqueduct	B	Apartment block
3	Atrium	C	Painting on wet plaster
4	Classical	D	Open-air stadium for gladiators
5	Domus	E	Open hall in a house
6	Forum	F	Country house of the rich
7	Fresco	G	A bridge for transporting water
8	Insula	H	Roman-style architecture and sculpture
9	Stola	I	Patrician's house
10	Villa	J	Marketplace

1	
2	
3	
4	
5	
6	
7	
8	
9	
10	

3 What is the meaning of the following Latin phrases? (Literacy)

caveat emptor		terra firma	
in absentia		bona fide	
status quo		NB (nota bene)	

4 What English words derive their origin from these Latin words? (Literacy)

anima		decimus	
carbo		liber	
corpus		mater	

5 Roman numerals

1 = I; 2 = II; 3 = III; 4 = IV; 5 = V; 6 = VI; 7 = VII; 8 = VIII; 9 = IX; 10 = X; 20 = XX; 50 = L; 100 = C (Numeracy)

Use the above to convert the following.

13 =	XXIV =
19 =	XXX =
24 =	XL =
59 =	LXXXIX =
115 =	CIV =

What are the problems with using Roman numerals today?

___

___

6 Which of the following statements about **Ancient Rome** are true, and which are false? Tick the appropriate boxes.

	True	False
Roman towns were built in a grid pattern, with streets at right angles to each other.		
The forum was the marketplace.		
Wealthy and powerful Romans were called plebeians.		
Most Romans were called patricians.		
The atrium was also called the *peristylium*.		
The Romans used little furniture in their houses.		
The walls were decorated with murals which were painted as frescoes, that is, they were made by painting on wet plaster.		
In the *insulae*, the lower storeys were built of stone, while the upper storeys were built of timber.		
The public fountains were supplied through aqueducts.		
The children were expected to obey their father even when they had grown up.		
Girls were allowed to marry at twelve years of age and boys at fourteen.		
Wealthy Roman men wore a stola over the tunic.		
Wealthy women wore a toga.		
Emperors gave a free supply of grain to 200,000 people every month to keep them happy.		
The main meal of richer Romans was called the cena.		
Gladiator contests were held in amphitheatres.		
The most popular sport was chariot-racing.		
In the public baths, body oil was scraped off with a strigil.		
Soldiers were the largest group working for the government.		
A legion was a group of about 100 soldiers.		
Cicero led the most serious slave rebellion.		
The Romans discovered and used concrete.		
Pillars, rounded arches and domes were features of classical architecture.		
Jupiter was the Father of the Gods.		
The dead person was rowed across the River Styx by Galaxy, the ferryman, to the underworld.		
Christians used the churches to hold ceremonies and bury their dead.		
The modern calendar is based on the calendar introduced by Julius Caesar in 46 BC.		

9 Medieval Society: Castle, Church and City

Key ideas

Feudalism – medieval system of land ownership; Normans invade England and later Ireland; impact – new laws, towns and cities; castles; new farming methods; new monastic style; English rule and language.

Fief – land granted by king to lords; vassal – received land from the lord in exchange for sworn loyalty; manor – village and land around it granted to the lords and knights.

Castles: motte and bailey castles – defence; shelter from attack; motte (mound), bailey (courtyard) with timber castle.

Stone castles – moat, curtain walls, battlements, towers, drawbridge, portcullis, gatehouse, bailey; keep – main tower of castle, steep steps, great hall, tapestries, feasts, spiral staircase, e.g. Trim Castle, Carrickfergus Castle.

Attacking castles – siege, machines, siege towers, scaling ladders, battering rams, undermining the wall.

Lord – fought for king, organised the castle, held court, hunted, hawked, feasted, musicians, jesters; lady – arranged marriage, dowry, running of castle, servants.

Knights – page, squire, dubbed, vows of chivalry, knighthood, lances, swords, tournaments, jousts, lord of manor.

Manor – village and land around manor house, moat; peasants (farmers), freemen, serfs; wattle and daub houses, lord's demesne; three-field system, farming; tithe; porridge, pottage.

Tower houses – replaced manor houses, similar to keep of castle, e.g. Ross Castle, Killarney.

Towns – at river crossings, routeways, coast, near castle; charter, walls, gates; merchants, craftsmen, workshops, guilds, apprentices, journeyman, masterpiece, markets, fairs – fair green, marketplace, market cross; curfew, punishment, stocks, pillory.

Monastery – diocese, cathedral, parish; church architecture – Romanesque, Gothic; Rule of St Benedict; almonry, cloister, scriptorium, manuscripts, chapter room, novice, tonsure; vows – chastity, poverty, obedience, prayer, abbot, almoner, refectory; Cistercians, Benedictines, Augustinians, new orders – friars, Dominicans, Franciscans.

Black Death – plague, black rats, third of population died.

1 Label the features of the medieval castle using the word list.

- drawbridge
- portcullis
- keep
- inner bailey
- outer bailey
- curtain wall
- moat
- workshops
- stables
- tower
- battlements
- steep steps

2 Medieval Research Project (✫ IT) (✫ Historical analysis)

Use both Google Earth and Google Maps (including street view and photographs) to examine evidence for medieval towns in Athenry, Co. Galway and/or Fethard, Co. Tipperary (or other towns in Ireland with medieval remains). Insert the information in short note form below.

	Evidence
Street names	
Religious buildings	
Defence	
Location	
Evidence of marketplace	
Other medieval features	
Evidence of modern development of the town	

3 Match up the following terms relating to the **Middle Ages** with their definitions. (✫ Literacy)

1	Abbot	A	Monastery dining room
2	Bailey	B	A deep drain around a castle
3	Town charter	C	An unfree peasant
4	Cloister	D	The first step to knighthood
5	Feudalism	E	Head of a monastery
6	Guild	F	Grid or gate in castle
7	Keep	G	Mound and timber castle
8	Manor	H	Authority from the king to levy taxes and to trade
9	Motte and bailey	I	A person who got land from a king or lord
10	Moat	J	Courtyard of a castle
11	Portcullis	K	A village and the land around it
12	Page	L	Organisation of craftsmen or merchants in towns
13	Refectory	M	Main tower in a castle
14	Serf	N	Medieval system of land ownership and defence
15	Vassal	O	A covered or open walkway in a monastery

1	
2	
3	
4	
5	
6	
7	
8	
9	
10	
11	
12	
13	
14	
15	

4 Writing a People in History answer. (✯ Communication)

Write about the person below. If you wish, you may use the hints to help you in your answer. Write the title at the top of the account.

(i) The Lady of the Castle in the Middle Ages

Hints: Early life; marriage to the lord; the castle; duties of the lady.

Hints are given in Ordinary Level People in History questions, but not in Higher Level questions

Writing the answer

Begin with a sentence stating who you are, e.g. I am a lady living in a castle in the Middle Ages. Say some more about who you are, e.g. give the name of a castle. Then write about your early life, but keep this to one sentence because you will only be awarded 2 or 3 marks for this introductory information before you become the lady. Then write about marriage to the lord and describe the castle. Use historical information in your answer, e.g. arranged marriage, increased power of lord, dowry; then go on to describing your castle, what the lord does, and your duties. (If you write carefully you could show how your castle survived an attack. Mention the role of the lady during the attack and use historical terms about the attack. You could also include viewing tournaments, attending feasts, and other features of castle life.) Use historical information or terms to fill out your answer. Make a list of those terms under each heading. Now you are ready to write.

8–10 significant historical statements

5 Read the extract below and answer the questions that follow. **Optional**

SOURCE ANALYSIS: DOCUMENTS

1489. November 14. Dublin. Written to Mayor and Bailiffs of Dublin, from Gerald, Earl of Kildare, Deputy to Jaspar, Duke of Bedford, Lieutenant of Ireland for Henry VII.

The King has been informed that dung-heaps, swine, hog-sties, and other nuisances in the streets, lanes and suburbs of Dublin infect the air and produce mortality, fevers, and pestilence throughout the city. Many citizens and sojourners have thus died in Dublin. The fear of pestilence prevents the coming thither of bards, ecclesiastics and lawyers. Great detriments thence arise to his Majesty, as well as the dangers to his subject and impediments to business. The King commands the Mayor and Bailiffs to cause forthwith the removal of all swine, and to have the streets and lanes freed from ordure, so as to prevent the loss of life from pestilential exhalations. The Mayor is to expel all Irish vagrants and mendicants from the city, and to execute his office for the preservation of the peace and proper administration of justice.

Henry VII 1489

(*Source*: Dublinia Heritage Centre)

(i) Read the extract carefully using the definitions below.

dung = animal manure; swine = pigs; hog-sties = enclosures for pigs; mortality = death; pestilence = disease; sojourners = visitors; thither = to that place; bards = poets; ecclesiastics = clergy, priests; detriments = harm; subject = a person under the rule of the king; impediments = obstruction; ordure = dung, manure; exhalations = breathing out; vagrants = people who wander about with no job or home; mendicants = beggars; execute his office = carry out his duties

(ii) Underline the key ideas in the extract.

(iii) Write a summary of the extract in your own words.

____

____

____

____

____

____

____

(iv) Mention at least one difficulty historians face in researching medieval documents.

____

(v) How can they overcome this difficulty/these difficulties?

____

(vi) Is this a primary or a secondary source? Explain your answer.

____

(vii) Using information from the extract, explain one difference between Dublin in 1489 and Dublin (or any other Irish city or town) today.

____

❻ **Label and circle each of the features below from the word list.**

battering ram; word; jousting; knight; crossbow; longbow; catapult; shield; siege tower; helmet; scaling ladder; lance; crest, battlements.

10 The Renaissance

Key ideas

Renaissance – revival of interest in learning of ancient Greece and Rome: causes – ruins of ancient Rome, city-states, wealth of city-states, fall of Constantinople, printing press.

Differences in art – medieval art – religious theme, lifeless, egg yolk, wood panels, no depth, fresco, Gothic architecture; Renaissance art – many themes, religious, legends, portraits, lifelike, oil, canvas, perspective, fresco, Roman-style architecture.

Lorenzo de Medici – patron, Florence, collector of manuscripts, private library, Platonic Academy, school of sculpture.

Gutenberg – German, goldsmith, moveable metal type, printing press, 42-line Bible, method of printing, effects – more books, cheaper, literacy, more education, new ideas spread.

Leonardo da Vinci – all-round genius, Florence, apprentice to Master Verrocchio, Milan, *The Virgin of the Rocks*, sfumato, *The Last Supper*, notebooks – astronomy, geology, engineering, anatomy, *Mona Lisa* in Florence, died in France.

Michelangelo – Florence, Master Ghirlandaio, school of sculpture, *Pietà* in Rome, *David* in Florence, ceiling of Sistine Chapel, *The Last Judgement*, dome of St Peter's Basilica.

Dürer – German, engraver, court painter to Emperor Maximilian, self-portraits, plants – *Large Clod*, animals – *Young Hare*, engravings – *Four Horsemen of the Apocalypse*, *St Jerome in his Study*, *The Knight, Death and the Devil*.

Galileo – pendulum and clock, professor of mathematics, theory of falling bodies, telescope, mountains and craters on moon, moons of Jupiter, sunspots, supported Copernicus' theory of sun at centre of universe, Inquisition, 'Father of Modern Science', Kepler, Newton.

Shakespeare – Stratford-on-Avon, wrote in vernacular, Anne Hathaway, Globe Theatre in London, actor, playwright, thirty-eight plays; tragedies, e.g. *Hamlet*, *Macbeth*; comedies, e.g. *The Merchant of Venice*; histories, e.g. *Henry V*, *Julius Caesar*; poet, sonnets, plays performed in daylight, died in Stratford-on-Avon.

Influence of the Renaissance – questioning spirit, new knowledge in science, medicine and geography, led to the Age of Exploration and the Reformation, developments in painting, sculpture and architecture, printing press spread education and literacy.

1 Match up the beginning and end of these sentences on the **causes of the Renaissance in Italy.** Historical analysis

1	The Renaissance was the rebirth or revival	A	of their glorious past.
2	At this time, Italy	B	and brought their manuscripts with them.
3	Before Constantinople was captured, many scholars left for Italy	C	could now be spread more rapidly all over Europe.
4	Ancient Roman ruins reminded Italians	D	and used this wealth to become patrons of the arts.
5	The learning of ancient Greece and Rome	E	of interest in the learning of ancient Greece and Rome.
6	Humanists believed that the writings of ancient Greece and Rome	F	was made up of many small states.
7	Italian merchants became rich	G	gave a greater understanding of human nature.

1	
2	
3	
4	
5	
6	
7	

2 Match the following terms relating to the **Renaissance** with the definitions. (☆ Literacy)

1	Apprentice	A	Painting on wet plaster
2	Classical	B	Showing depth in paintings
3	Fresco	C	Blending colours for shading
4	Gothic	D	In the native or local language
5	Patron	E	Roman-style art and architecture
6	Perspective	F	Medieval-style art and architecture
7	Sfumato	G	Learning to be a master painter
8	Vernacular	H	Supporter of artists

1	
2	
3	
4	
5	
6	
7	
8	

3 Differences in Art

Classify each of the following features of art by inserting them in the boxes under **Medieval Art** and **Renaissance Art** below. (Some may go in both.)

Greek and Roman legends · dome · pointed arches · oil · Gothic style of architecture · realistic · wood panels · canvas · three-dimensional · Roman style of architecture · religious message · nature and landscape · egg yolk · rounded arches · no life or emotion · perspective · frescoes · faces similar · lacked depth · part of cathederal · variety of colours · portraits of leaders · rose window

Medieval Art	Renaissance Art
______________________	______________________
______________________	______________________
______________________	______________________
______________________	______________________
______________________	______________________
______________________	______________________
______________________	______________________
______________________	______________________
______________________	______________________
______________________	______________________

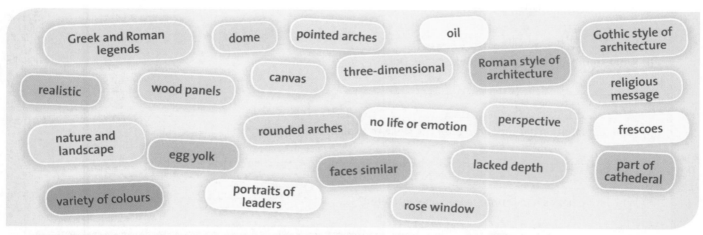

4 Extract on Leonardo da Vinci

Read the extract and the answer the following questions.

SOURCE ANALYSIS: DOCUMENT

An extract from Giorgio Vasari's *Life of Leonardo da Vinci* written in 1550 and revised in 1568

The Prior kept urging Leonardo to finish his work; for it seemed strange to him to see Leonardo sometimes stand half a day at a time, lost in thought, and he would have liked him to go on like the labourers hoeing in the garden, without ever stopping his brush. He complained of it to the Duke, who sent for Leonardo and delicately urged him to work.

Leonardo explained to the Duke that men of lofty genius sometimes accomplish the most when they work least, seeking out inventions with the mind, and forming those perfect ideas, which the hands afterwards express. He told the Duke he still had two heads to paint; that of Christ, which he did not wish to seek on earth; and he could not think that it was possible to imagine that beauty and heavenly grace which should be the face of God's son.

Next, there was the head of Judas, which was also troubling him, not thinking himself capable of imagining features that should represent the face of him who had a mind so cruel as to resolve to betray his Lord, the creator of the world. However, he would seek out a model for Judas; but if in the end he could not find better, he might consider the foolish Prior. This moved the Duke wondrously to laughter, and he said that Leonardo had a thousand reasons on his side. And so the poor Prior, in confusion, confined himself to urging on the work in the garden and left Leonardo in peace.

(i) What complaint did the Prior make to the Duke?

____

____

(ii) What explanation did Leonardo offer the Duke to explain his slow progress?

____

____

(iii) Which two heads had Leonardo not yet completed?

____

(iv) What is the name of the painting referred to in the above extract?

____

(v) From your study of the Renaissance, give two reasons why wealthy merchants, rulers and Popes were willing to sponsor artists.

____

____

(vi) Is this account by Vasari favourable or unfavourable to Leonardo? Explain your answer.

____

____

(vii) Is this a primary or a secondary source? Explain your answer.

____

5 Which of the following statements are **causes and which are results/effects** of the Renaissance? ✩ Historical analysis

Events	Causes	Effects/results
Italian cities grew rich with trade.		
Italian artists became famous.		
Vernacular languages benefited.		
Italian cities competed with each other.		
The Renaissance spread to Northern Europe through trade routes.		
Ancient Roman sculptors could be seen in many parts of Italy.		
A questioning spirit caused the Reformation.		
Explorers wanted to gain greater geographical knowledge.		
Printing press invented		
Sfumato technique developed by Leonardo		
Revival of interest in the learning of Ancient Greece and Rome		

6 Google these key events of the Renaissance (A to H) below and mark them on the timeline. ✩ Numeracy ✩ IT

	Events	Dates
A	Michelangelo painted the ceiling of the Sistine Chapel.	
B	Leonardo da Vinci painted the *Mona Lisa*.	
C	Gutenberg invented the printing press.	
D	The death of Lorenzo the Magnificent.	
E	Dürer painted *The Hare*.	
F	Shakespeare wrote *Hamlet*.	
G	Galileo designed his telescope.	
H	Michelangelo sculpted the *Pietá*.	

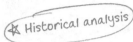

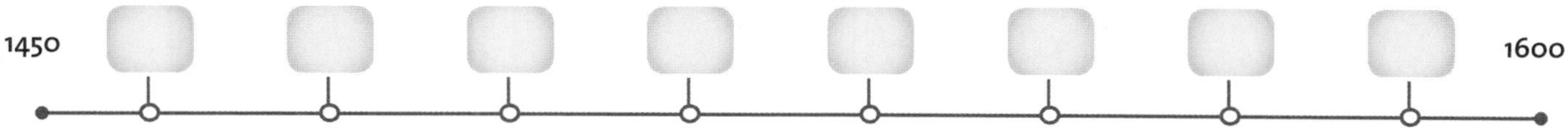

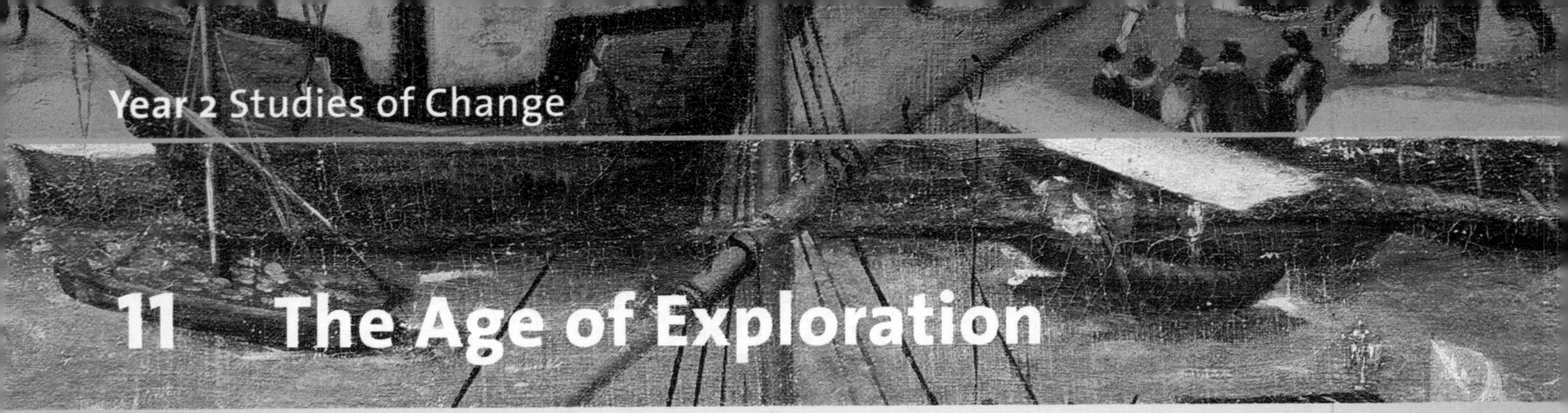

11 The Age of Exploration

Key ideas

Causes – influence of Renaissance – geographical knowledge; new trade routes to East; Marco Polo; wealth for countries; wealth for explorers; religion.

Ships and navigation – caravels – lateen and square sails; carvel-built; rudder; compass; quadrant, astrolabe, cross-staff – latitude; maps; log and line; lead and line; sandglass; logbook; dangers for sailors – scurvy.

Portuguese voyages – causes – religion, Prester John; trade; Prince Henry the Navigator – school for navigation, Sagres, voyages along African coast; padrão (pillar); slaves and gold; Diaz – Cape of Good Hope; da Gama – India; results – defeated Arabs – control of spice trade; Portuguese empire and culture.

Voyage of Christopher Columbus – Italian – Genoa; reasons – world round, world smaller; go west to get to East; trade; religion; Ferdinand and Isabella of Spain; three ships – *Santa María, Niña, Pinta*; Admiral of the Ocean Sea; Palos; Canary Islands; two distances travelled; trade winds; San Salvador, Cuba, Hispaniola; *Santa María* ran aground; La Navidad; Results – further voyages; settlers, sugar cane; cruelty to natives; spread of Spanish culture; New World, called America after Amerigo Vespucci; Treaty of Tordesillas.

Voyage of Magellan – Portuguese; el Paso; Spice Islands in Spanish half?; Charles V; five ships – governor and profits; Seville; Canary Islands; South America – El Paso, Straits of Magellan; Pacific Ocean, scurvy, death; Philippine Islands, death of Magellan; del Cano to Spain in *Victoria*; first complete world voyage; world round; Spice Islands in Portuguese half.

Cortes and Pizarro – conquistadors; *Cortés and Aztecs*, Mexico; god; Tenochtitlán – capital; Montezuma – ruler; conflict; Cortés captured capital and empire; colonisation; New Spain; **Pizarro and Incas**, Peru; Atahualpa – ruler; captured by Spanish; room full of gold and silver; killed; Cuzco – capital; Pizarro captured capital and empire; gold and silver mines; slave labour; Spanish ships attacked by English; war.

Results – geographical knowledge; decay of empires – Aztecs, Incas; rise of European empires; Spanish architecture and land system in South America; decline of Mediterranean; rise of Atlantic – Britain, France, Holland; war between European powers; spread of Christianity; slavery; new food; effects on colonies/Europe.

1 The Causes of the Age of Exploration ☆ Historical skills

Look at the mind map of the **Causes of the Age of Exploration** on the next page. Fill in the spaces in the boxes from the word list below. Some of the boxes have been filled in already.

Word list: Questioning spirit; Arab & Italian controlled; Wealth for countries; Convert people to Christianity; Silk & jewels; Great Silk Road; Defeat Muslims; New trade routes; Ptolemy's *Geographia*; Wealth; Glory; Power; Marco Polo; World round; Travels to China; Wealth & fame for explorers; Influence of the Renaissance; spices; Riches and tithes; Religion.

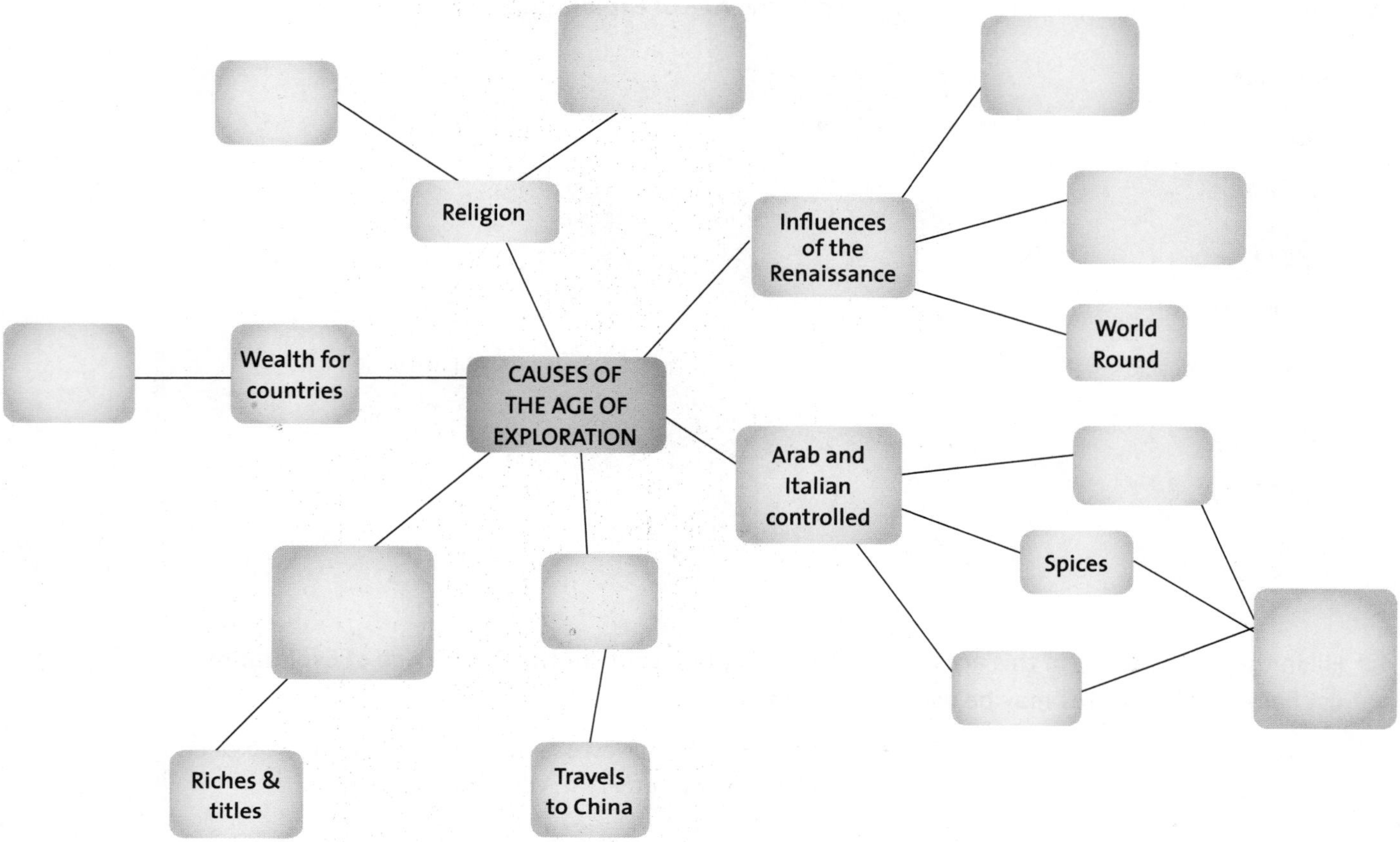

❷ Match each explanation with the corresponding Key Term. ☆ Literacy

1	Used in ships of the Age of Exploration to record events during the voyage	A	Carvel-built
2	Triangular sails used on caravels	B	Quadrant
3	When people from one country settle in another country	C	Portolan charts
4	Hull of ship with planks edge-to-edge	D	Caravel
5	Earliest maps used during the Age of Exploration	E	Lateen
6	Navigation instrument used in the Age of Exploration to find latitude	F	Logbook
7	Ship used by Portuguese and Spanish to explore coasts of Africa and America	G	Colonisation

1	
2	
3	
4	
5	
6	
7	

❸ Explain each of the following terms relating to **the Age of Exploration.** (☆ Literacy)

Astrolabe	
Padrão	
Scurvy	
Rudder	
Conquistadors	
Treaty of Tordesillas	
Spices	
Compass	
El Paso	

❹ Fill in the blank spaces in this account of the **Portuguese contribution to the Age of Exploration** from the word list below. (Some words may be used more than once.)

Word List: Sagres; da Gama; astrolabe; Henry; Azores; India; slaves; Bojador; shipbuilders; *padrãos*; gold; Leone; Prester; Muslims; navigation; caravel; Africa; Morocco; fifteenth; Diaz; Verde; Muslim; African.

The leader of the Portuguese explorations was Prince ______________ the Navigator, third son of the King of Portugal. He believed in the legend of ______________ John and he wanted to conquer the ______________. He set up a school for ______________ in ______________ in southern Portugal. He invited mapmakers, ______________ and astronomers to plan the voyages along the coast of ______________. They gathered information on ______________ instruments – the ______________, the quadrant and the cross-staff – and contributed to the development of the ______________. The Portuguese led the way in the Age of Exploration, which began in the ______________ century when they drove the ______________ out of their country. They attacked ______________ strongholds in ______________ and heard about ______________ mines further south. They also heard about a great Christian kingdom in Africa, led by a king called ______________ John. The Portuguese thought that if they could join forces with him, then the two Christian armies would defeat the ______________. The Portuguese believed they would profit from trade. Prince ______________ sent ships south along the ______________ coast. The captains set up stone pillars on the coasts, called ______________, to mark the end of each voyage. They returned with ______________ and gold to help pay for the voyages. When Prince ______________ died in 1460, the Portuguese had sailed beyond Cape ______________ in modern-day ______________, and gone as far as Sierra ______________. The Portuguese also discovered the ______________, the Canary Islands and the Cape ______________ Islands. However, they still had a long way to go before rounding the southern tip of Africa. But in two great voyages led by Bartholomew ______________ and Vasco ______________, the Portuguese rounded Africa and sailed on until they reached ______________.

5 Put the following statements in chronological order, beginning with the earliest. (Numeracy)

	Statements	Dates	Order
1	Cortes to Mexico		
2	Columbus in San Salvador		
3	Diaz round the Cape of Good Hope		
4	Death of Magellan		
5	Treaty of Tordesillas		
6	Da Gama to India		
7	The Travels of Marco Polo		

6 Match the places with the explorers associated with them.

1	Henry the Navigator	A	Hispaniola	1	
2	Diaz	B	El Dorado	2	
3	Da Gama	C	Cape Bojador	3	
4	Early Portuguese explorers	D	Tenochtitlan	4	
5	Columbus	E	Sagres	5	
6	Magellan	F	Calicut	6	
7	Cortes	G	Cape of Storms	7	
8	Pizarro	H	Pacific Ocean	8	
9	Spanish expedition down the Amazon	I	Cuzco	9	

7 The caravel and carvel-built

SOURCE ANALYSIS: PICTURES & DOCUMENTS

Also known as: *carvel*; *caravela*
From: *Encyclopedia of Exploration*, vol. 2.

DOCUMENT A

Caravels were light and maneuverable ships with two or, more commonly, three masts. They typically had a lateen rig, but their front two masts could be square-rigged to take advantage of the prevailing winds in open seas. They were most often carvel-built, a type of construction in which planks are shaped to be flush edge to edge, with caulked seams, rather than overlapping planks as in clinker-built technology. This design feature reduced friction between hull and water. Caravels had flat sterns and center rudders like other European ships. Their sizes varied, the smallest about 60 tons and the largest exceeding 200 tons.

The caravel's hull could resist the pounding of waves; its shallow draught allowed for coastal navigation; and its triangular sails could take advantage of a variety of winds. While the caravel was easy to control and dependable in rough weather, it was not the most comfortable of ships.

(*Source*: Waldman, Carl, and Jon Cunningham, 'caravel,' *Encyclopedia of Exploration: Places, Technologies, and Cultural Trends*, volume 2. New York: Facts On File, Inc., 2004)

DOCUMENT B

Clinker-built ships: Northern ships were clinker-built. That is, their hulls were made of overlapping planks hand cut with adzes. This was for a very simple reason – they had not invented the saw. The system worked very well and only had one problem – on ships longer than 100 feet joining the planks became too difficult.

Mediterranean-style: Southern or Mediterranean ships had their hulls made in the carvel fashion. Their smooth-sided wooden planks were fitted edge to edge over a frame and sealed with caulking in between. The Southerners could do this because they had saws and could make square-cut planks.

The carvel-type ships suffered a serious drawback in that they were difficult to make water-tight and water constantly seeped in. Their advantage was that they could be made to any length.

Eventually by 1350 the northern and Mediterranean styles combined to form a sturdy, faster and larger open-ocean going vessel. It was carvel built for extra length, had both square sail (for power) and lanteen (for manoeuvrability close to land and faster tacking) and a castle fore and aft. They also had the straight stern-post and stern-rudder.

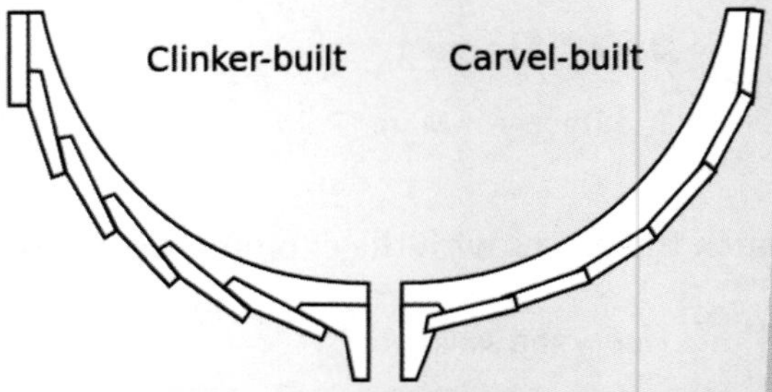

(*Source*: *The History of Sailing Ships*, www.abc.net.au/navigators/ships/historyeuro.htm)

Document A

(i) What features had the caravel, according to Document A?

____

(ii) How did these features make the caravel suitable for exploring?

____

____

Document B

(iii) What is the difference between clinker-built and carvel-built, according to Document B?

____

(iv) Why were Northern ships clinker-built, according to Document B?

____

(v) Why were Mediterranean-ships carvel-built?

____

(vi) What were the advantages of the carvel-built ship, according to Document B?

____

(vii) How do the advantages of the caravel listed in Document A compare with the advantages listed in Document B?

____

____

____

8 Mark the places from (A) to (I) below into this map.

(A) Spain and Portugal (B) Cape of Good Hope (C) Spice Islands (D) China (E) Da Gama's voyage
(F) Columbus's first voyage (G) Aztec empire (H) Inca empire (I) Line of Tordesillas

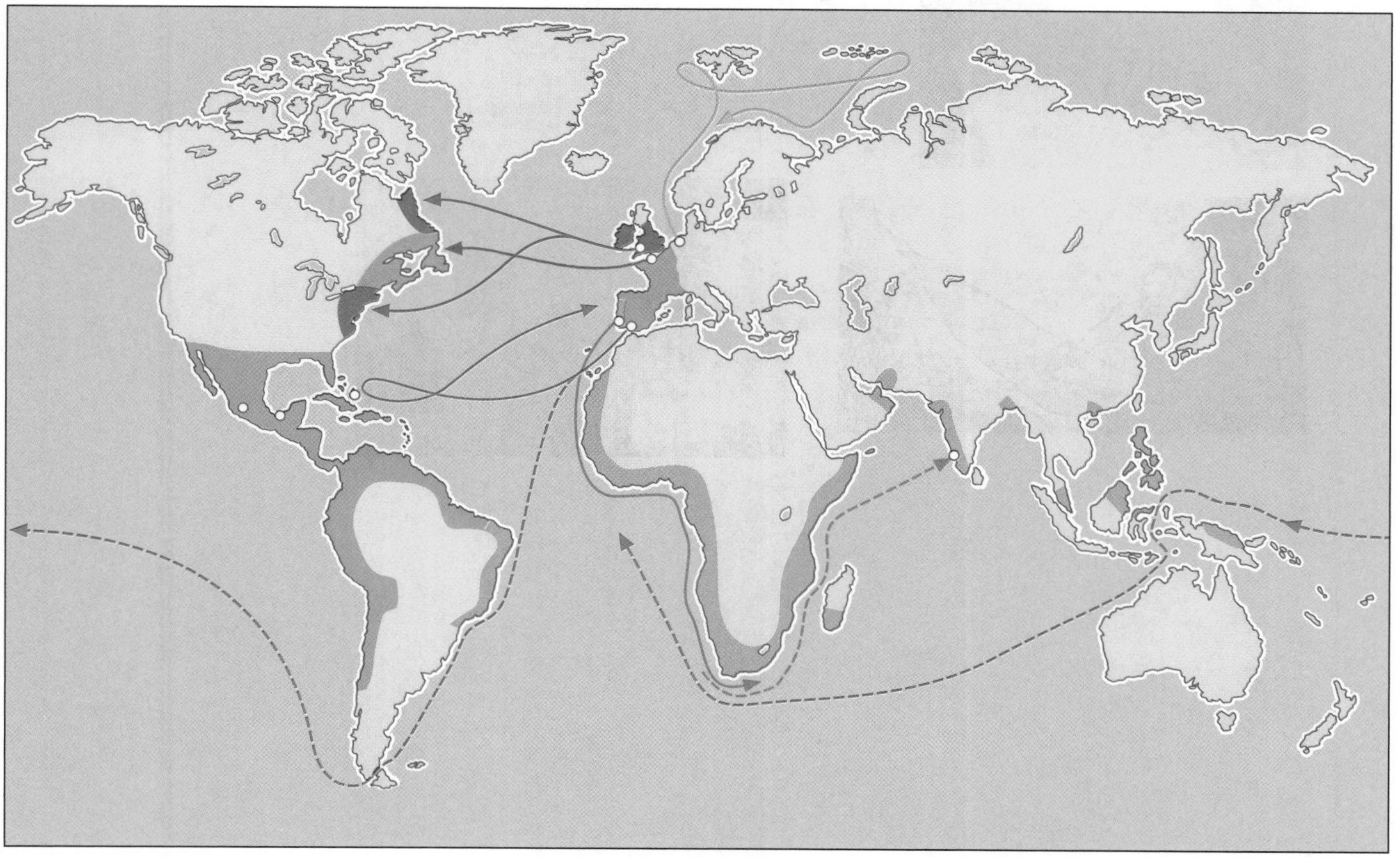

9 Identify the following features associated with the Age of Exploration.

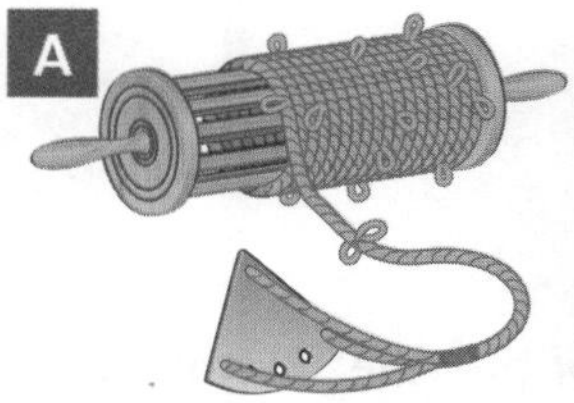

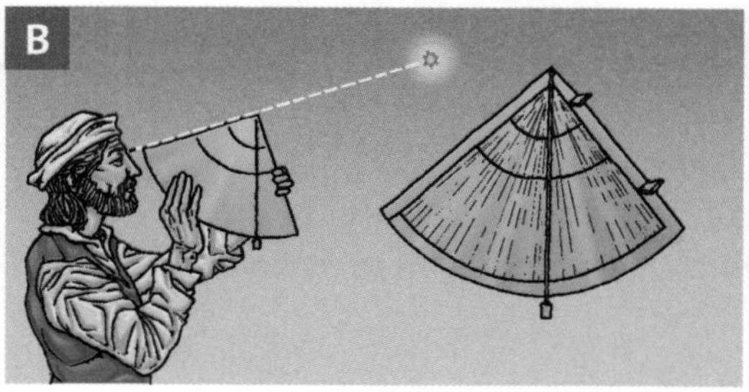

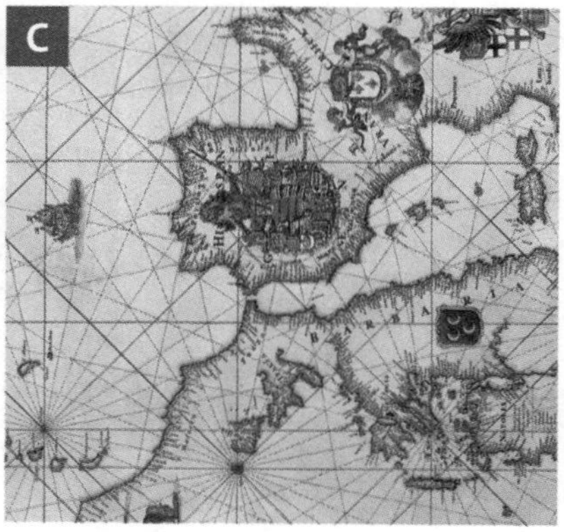

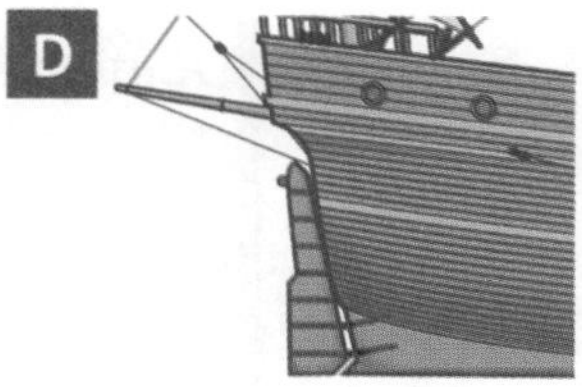

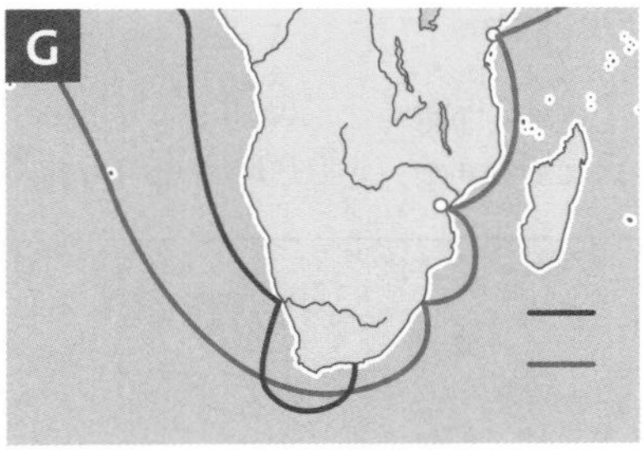

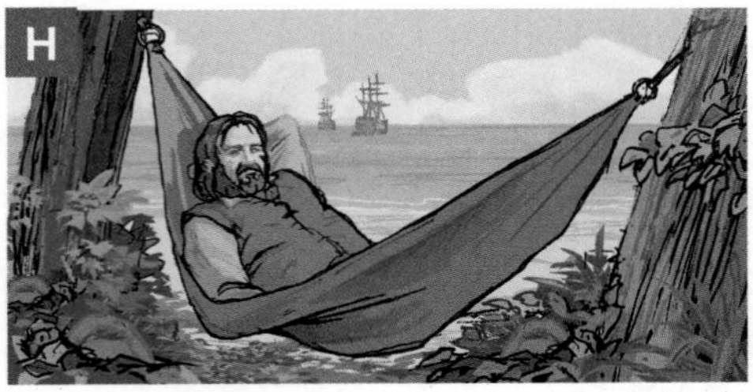

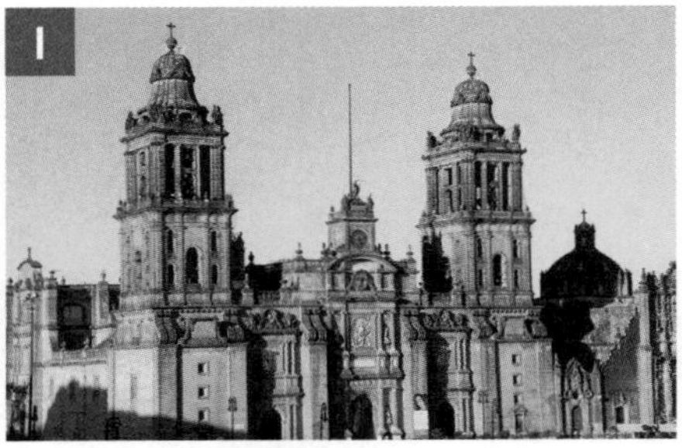

A	
B	
C	
D	
E	
F	
G	
H	
I	

Historical analysis Literacy

10 The Results of the Age of Exploration

Which of the following is a **fact** and which is an **opinion** in relation to the **results of the Age of Exploration**? Tick the correct answer.

	Fact	Opinion
(i) Portugal and Spain were the first European countries to establish great empires.		
(ii) The Arab and Italian control of trade was broken.		
(iii) European culture was spread to the New World.		
(iv) Slavery was good for Africa and the New World.		
(v) Mexico and Peru were helped by the spread of Spanish culture.		

11 Which of the following statements in relation to the **results of the Age of Exploration** are true and which are false? Tick the correct answer.

	True	False
(i) The Age of Exploration led to wars between Britain and Spain and France and Spain.		
(ii) London, Venice and Amsterdam increased in prosperity.		
(iii) Most trade shifted to the Atlantic coast of Europe.		
(iv) New foods which Europeans had not seen before, for example sugar cane, were brought from the New World.		
(v) The old geographical ideas Europeans had about the world were shown to be wrong.		
(vi) The Spanish land system based on the hacienda was used to control the native people of the Americas.		
(vii) Spain, France and Portugal spread the Protestant religion in the New World.		

12 Focus Task (☆ IT)

Create a **Fakebook page** for **Christopher Columbus** at www.classtools.net/**FAKEBOOK**

Use information from your textbook and from Christopher Columbus, www.flmnh.ufl.edu/caribarch/columbus.htm.

12 The Reformation

Key ideas

Causes of Reformation – wealth of Catholic Church; abuses – nepotism, simony, pluralism, absenteeism; bad organisation; influence of the Renaissance; the printing press; power of kings and princes.

Martin Luther – Professor of Theology, Wittenberg University; salvation – faith alone; Tetzel, sale of indulgences; 95 Theses; Cardinal Cajetan; John Eck; papal bull – excommunication; Charles V, Diet of Worms; Frederick the Wise, translation of New Testament; Protestants; marriage – Katherine von Bora. Results – Germany divided, use of vernacular language, increased literacy and education, religious wars.

John Calvin – French; converted to Protestantism; wrote *The Institutes of the Christian Religion*; set up church in Geneva; beliefs – predestination, the Bible, two sacraments – baptism and Eucharist; Geneva – city of God; run by pastors (ministers), teachers, deacons, elders; strict rules – no drunkenness, bawdy songs, card or dice playing; plain dress; plain churches; schools and university – spread of Calvin's religion – Scotland (John Knox), France (Huguenots), England (Puritans), Holland.

Reformation in England – Henry VIII – wanted to annul marriage to Catherine of Aragon and to marry Anne Boleyn, Pope refused, Henry passed Act of Supremacy – head of Church of England; Oath of Supremacy; closure of the monasteries – said they were badly run, wanted wealth, loyal to the Pope; 370 closed, income from rents, loyal nobility; Bible in English but no other changes. Edward VI – Protestantism developed, Book of Common Prayer. Mary – return to Catholic religion but monasteries still closed. Elizabeth – Church of England (Anglican), Protestantism established.

Reformation in Ireland – similar changes by Henry VIII, Edward VI, Mary and Elizabeth; but failure to convert Ireland to Protestantism – part of English conquest, use of English language, influence of Catholic Counter-Reformation. English and Scottish Protestants as planters.

Catholic Counter-Reformation – **Council of Trent** – reformed Catholic Church; beliefs – faith and good works needed for salvation, Bible and teachings of Church, seven sacraments, priests special people, cannot marry, Pope head of church; discipline – old abuses banned, catechism, images of Christ, Mary and saints in churches; results – Catholicism strengthened, greater divisions between religions.

Jesuits – Ignatius of Loyola; wrote Spiritual Exercises; Jesuits organised like an army – strict discipline; preaching, deeds of charity, teaching – schools for sons of nobles and merchants; missionaries – Francis Xavier to India and Japan; strengthened Catholicism.

Court of Inquisition – court of Catholic Church in Spain and Italy; punished people accused of heresy (beliefs against the Catholic Church); used torture, spying, punishment – wore San Benito, whipped, burned at stake; Protestantism crushed in Spain and Italy.

Results of Reformation – Counter-Reformation – Catholic Church efforts to stop the spread of Protestantism (Council of Trent, Jesuits, Inquisition) – Europe divided on religion, northern Germany and northern Europe largely Protestant; southern Europe and Ireland largely Catholic; religious differences spread to empires, e.g. Spanish South America Catholic; English North America largely Protestant; Reformation in England – closure of monasteries, Anglican Church; wars of religion – civil wars in France, Germany (Holy Roman Empire); wars between countries, e.g. England and Spain – Spanish Armada; Thirty Years War in Europe; intolerance and persecution; differences in art and architecture – plain churches v. Baroque Catholic churches; spread of education.

❶ Martin Luther

Word List: Worried about salvation; Half to Archbishop of Mainz; Justification by faith; In Latin; Printed in German; Sale of indulgences; Indulgences do not save people; Papal Bull; Augustinian Order; Literacy & education; Cardinal Cajetan; Professor of Theology; Diet of Worms; Calvinism; Wartburg Castle; Germany divided; Edict of Worms; Protestant Northern Europe; New Testament translated; Vernacular literature.

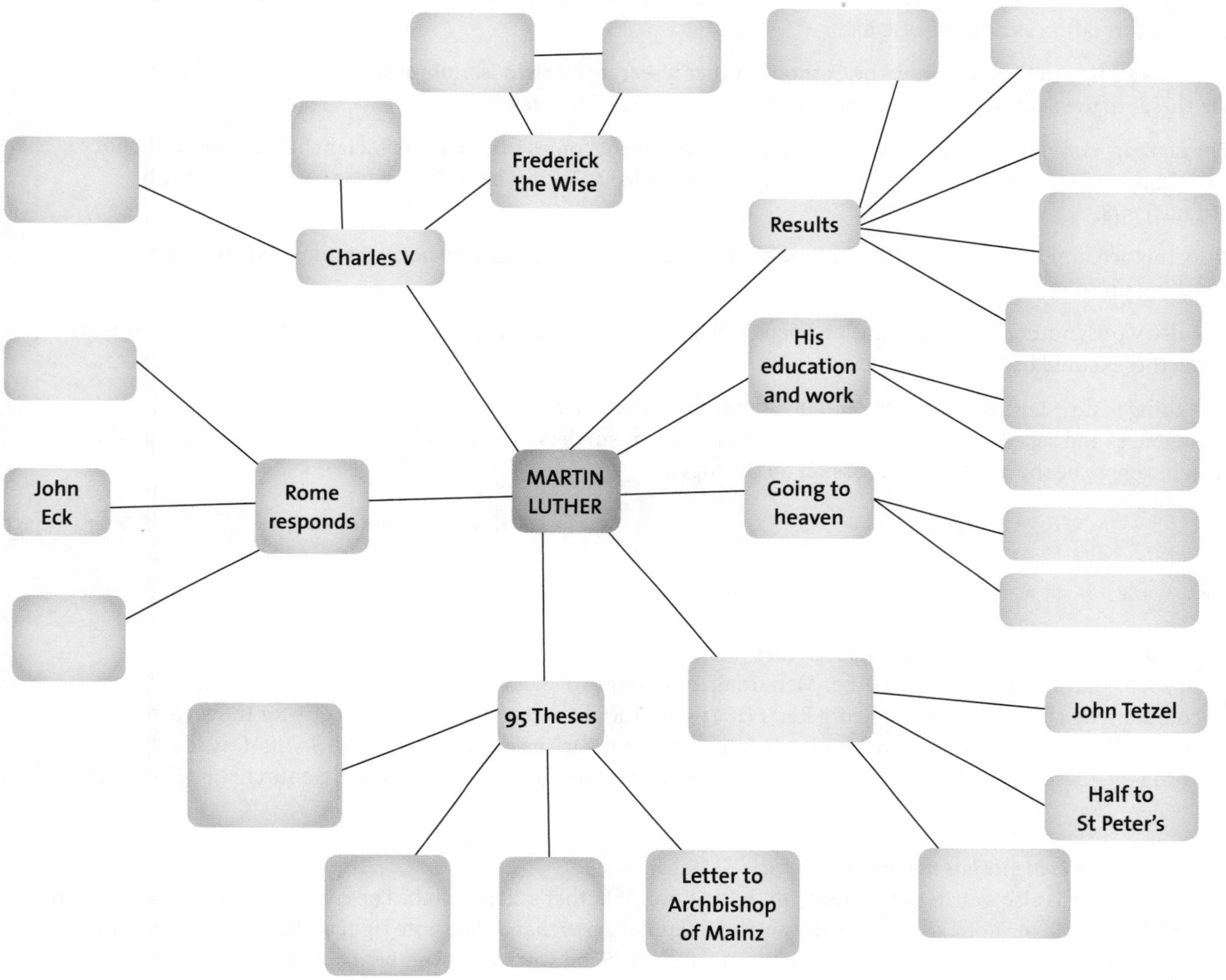

2 Did Luther nail 95 Theses on the church door in Wittenberg?
Read the documents A–C and answer the questions that follow.

SOURCE ANALYSIS: DOCUMENTS

DOCUMENT A: LEGENDS ABOUT LUTHER: NAILING THE 95 THESES

October 31, 1517: Luther nailing his 95 Theses to the door of the Castle Church in Wittenberg has become a symbol of the Reformation as nothing else has.

It was like a slap in the face when the Catholic Luther researcher, Erwin Iserloh, asserted in 1961 that the nailing of the theses to the door of the Castle Church belonged to the realm of legends.

The facts are convincing, the first written account of the event comes from Philipp Melanchthon who could not have been an eye-witness to the event since he was not called to Wittenberg University as a professor until [August] 1518.

Also, this account appeared for the first time after Luther's death [1546] and he never commented on 'nailing anything up' in 1517.

It is also worth noting, that there was no open discussion of the theses in Wittenberg and that no original printing of the theses could be found.

One thing is sure: Luther wrote a letter to his superiors on October 31, 1517 in which he denounced the sale of indulgences and asked for repayment and removal of the misunderstandings. With the letter he included 95 theses which were to be the basis for a discussion on the topic.

(*Source*: www.luther.de/en/legenden/tanschl.html)

DOCUMENT B: ON THE DOORS OF THE WITTENBERG CHURCHES

The unnoticed comment by Luther's secretary
In 2006, Martin Treu from the Luther Memorials Foundation of Saxony-Anhalt rediscovered a handwritten comment by Luther's secretary Georg Rörer (1492–1557). Right at the end of the desk copy for the revision of the New Testament in 1540, Rörer made the following note: 'On the evening before All Saints' Day in the year of our Lord 1517, theses about letters of indulgence were nailed to the doors of the Wittenberg churches by Doctor Martin Luther.'

The ultimate evidence has not been produced
Now Rörer was also not an eye-witness, but he was one of Luther's closest staff. The copy of the New Testament, in which he made his note, contains many entries in Luther's own hand. The note right at the end of the volume leads us to assume that it was made at the conclusion of the revision work in November 1544. Rörer's reference to the Wittenberg churches in the plural must be emphasised, as it corresponds to the statutes of the university. According to these, all public announcements had to be nailed to the doors of the churches.

While this does not give final proof of the theses being nailed to the door, together with Rörer's note it seems much more probable. It is at least so far the oldest source for it from the time when Luther was still alive. And: Wittenberg now has more than one 'Theses Door'.

(*Source*: www.luther2017.de/en/627-doors-wittenberg-churches?contid=7349)

DOCUMENT C: LUTHER HIMSELF NEVER MENTIONS ANYTHING

Luther himself never mentions anything about nailing the 95 Theses to the church door but rather explains how they were sent out to particular ecclesiastical authorities. The first bit of evidence is Luther's letter (or cover letter) to Albrecht from October 31, 1517 (LW 48:43) sent with a copy of the 95 Theses. [Then] in a letter dated November 21, 1518 to Elector Frederick [of Saxony], Luther states, '[S]*ome liars among ourselves falsely assert that I undertook the disputation on the Indulgences by your Grace's advice, when the fact is, that not even my dearest friends were aware of it.*' He also states that previous to the 95 Theses becoming public, he sent two letters (to the Archbishop of Magdeburg/Mainz and the Bishop of Brandenburg). So from Luther's own accounts, he never mentions nailing the 95 Theses to the Wittenberg door. William Pauck notes, '*Luther, who had a tendency to speak freely about his career and who, in his later years, loved to reminisce, never mentioned the incident. Moreover, there are no other contemporary sources which support the old story.*' [Olin, John (ed.) *Luther, Erasmus and the Reformation*].

(*Source*: beggarsallreformation.blogspot.ie/2011/10/95-theses-nailed-to-church-door-or.html)

(i) What arguments are put forward in Document A against Luther nailing the 95 Theses on the church door?

(ii) What arguments are put forward in Document B in favour of Luther nailing the 95 Theses on the church door?

(iii) What arguments are put forward in Document C against Luther nailing the 95 Theses on the church door?

(iv) Are there primary sources used in each of the Documents? Explain your answer.

(v) Which view do you support based on the above documents? Explain your answer.

Summarise the main points in your answer to question (v) here.

Please answer questions i–iv in your exercise copy.

3 Match each Key Term with the corresponding explanation. Literacy

1	Absenteeism	A	Efforts by the Catholic Church to reform itself and stop the spread of Protestantism
2	Simony	B	A release from punishment for sin
3	Nepotism	C	Bad practices common in the Catholic Church
4	Church abuses	D	Bishops and cardinals not living in their dioceses
5	Counter-Reformation	E	Using your power to get jobs for your family or relations
6	Indulgences	F	The buying and selling of church offices or positions

1	
2	
3	
4	
5	
6	

4 Causes of the Reformation

Match each sentence beginning in Column A with the appropriate ending in Column B. ☆ Historical skills

Column A		Column B	
1	In Germany, the Catholic Church owned about	A	the Bible for themselves.
2	There was dislike among the German people	B	behaved like princes.
3	Many scholars could now read	C	who were opposed to a church dominated by the sons of wealthy nobles.
4	Popes, cardinals and bishops	D	one-third of the land.
5	Kings were supported by a growing middle class	E	spread quickly through books and pamphlets.
6	Priests could not read	F	for paying extra taxes and church dues to an outside power in Rome.
7	Criticisms of the Catholic Church could be	G	the Bible or preach.

1	
2	
3	
4	
5	
6	
7	

5 Put these events in chronological order. Insert the letters in the correct order in the box to the right.

☆ Numeracy ☆ Chronology

Events		Dates	Order
A	The Jesuits were founded		
B	The Council of Trent began		
C	Henry VIII passed the Act of Supremacy		
D	Calvin wrote *The Institutes of the Christian Religion*		
E	Luther burnt the Papal Bull		
F	The Peace of Augsburg		
G	Elizabeth established the Anglican Church		
H	Diet of Worms held		
I	Pope Alexander VI became Pope		
J	The printing press was invented		

❻ Fill in the blank spaces below in the account of **John Calvin.**

John Calvin was born in F_____________ in 1509. He was reared as a C_____________ but when he studied the writings of Martin Luther and the Bible, he was converted to P_____________ He was forced to leave F_____________ because of his beliefs.

He went to Basel in S _____________ There he wrote a book called *The I_____________ of the C_____________ R_____________*, which stated his beliefs. Then he was invited to G_____________, a French-speaking city, to set up a new c_____________.

Calvin said that God had selected those who were to go to h_____________ and to hell. This was called p_____________ Those who were saved (went to heaven) were called the e_____________.

The B_____________ was the only source for the teachings of Christ.

There are two s_____________, baptism and the Eucharist.

Calvin believed that G_____________ was the City of G_____________, in contrast to Rome, which he looked upon as the City of the D_____________.

Calvin's church did not have any b_____________. Instead, his church was run by p_____________ (or ministers), t_____________, d_____________ and e_____________.

Calvin had strict rules and severe punishments – people could even be burned to death at the s_____________. In spite of the punishments, people followed Calvin because they believed he would lead them to h_____________. Soon Geneva became famous for its e_____________ system. It even had a university to train m_____________. Calvin trained French p_____________ who went back to France even though their lives were in danger. Within a short time there were one million Calvinists in France. French Calvinists were known as H_____________.

❼ Write a sentence of evidence in support of each of the following statements. (Historical analysis)

(i) Luther's actions divided Christianity.

____

(ii) The Catholic Church was badly in need of reform.

____

(iii) The Jesuits played an important part in the Counter-Reformation.

____

(iv) The Council of Trent strengthened the Catholic Church.

____

❽ **The Results of the Reformation – Using Key Ideas**

Historical skills | Communication

Write your own account of the **Results of the Reformation** using the words under **Results**, p. 50 above, without referring to your textbook.

Make each point and develop it

13 Plantations in Ireland

Key ideas

Ireland in 1500 – Tudor family ruled; the Pale around Dublin – only area directly controlled by English government; Anglo-Irish lordships – English common law, e.g. Fitzgeralds of Kildare; Gaelic Irish lordships – Brehon law, e.g. O'Neill's of Tyrone.

Tudor conquest – military conquest – costly; surrender and regrant – failure, cause of further conflict; new policy plantations – confiscate land, planters (settlers) from England and Scotland; centres of English language, culture and law.

Plantation of Laois–Offaly – first; conquest of O'Mores and O'Connors – threat to the Pale; ruler – Mary; two counties – Queen's County (Laois), King's County (Offaly); county towns – Maryborough (Portlaoise), Philipstown (Daingean); two-thirds of land for planters from England and the Pale, one-third near Shannon for loyal Gaelic Irish; 360 acres; failure – not enough planters; O'Mores and O'Connors attacked planters.

Plantation of Munster – ruler – Elizabeth; defeat of Desmonds – land confiscated; aim – centre of English civilisation, resist Spanish invasion, settle younger sons of nobility from southern England; land surveyed and mapped; total – 300,000 acres; estates – 4,000, 6,000, 8,000, 12,000 acres; undertakers – bring in English farmers and labourers, pay rent, defend themselves; Walter Raleigh – 42,000 acres; one-third settled, not enough English tenants, planters attacked during Nine Years War; new planters; new plantation towns, e.g. Killarney, Bandon, Mallow; new farming methods, new breeds of sheep, cattle, increased trade.

Plantation of Ulster – defeat of O'Neill, O'Donnell, Flight of the Earls, land confiscated; ruler – James I; six counties, 4 million acres, land surveyed, mapped – crown land, church land; aims – loyal Protestant population, money from rents, pay soldiers and officials after Nine Years War; 1,000, 1,500, 2,000 acres; undertakers, servitors, loyal Irish; bawns, stone houses, stone castles; Plantation of Londonderry – London merchants, Irish Society, Coleraine, Derry; Success? Most successful, more English law, language, farming, loyal Protestant population – Presbyterians, Church of England; conflict with Gaelic Irish – land and religion, 1641 massacre, conflict into 19th and 20th centuries; new planned towns; new farming methods; increased trade.

Cromwellian Plantation – conquest by Cromwell; aims – crush Catholic religion, punish rebel leaders, pay off parliament's debts to adventurers and soldiers; rebel landowners lost all land; those who could not prove loyalty transplanted to Connacht and Clare; farmers, labourers not disturbed; Down Survey – 11 million acres; Success? Failed to crush Catholic religion; Catholic landowners lost land, Protestant ownership, Catholics forbidden to live in towns.

Overall results – Religious – Ireland more Protestant, Protestant landowners, Catholic tenants, labourers. Political – conflict over land and religion; penal laws; conflict into 19th and 20th centuries. Cultural – decline of Gaelic culture and language; English common law instead of Brehon law; new farming methods; more urban society.

1 Match the key terms in Column A with the explanation in Column B. (Literacy)

Column A		Column B	
1	Bawn	A	A country controlled by a more powerful country
2	Protestant Ascendancy	B	English planters who got land during the Plantation of Munster, or English and Scottish planters who got land during the Plantation of Ulster
3	Servitors	C	Policy of English government to bring in English and Scottish planters to Ireland
4	Undertakers	D	Walled enclosure built for defence in the Plantation of Ulster
5	Plantation	E	English soldiers and officials who were granted land in the Plantation of Ulster
6	Colony	F	Church of Ireland ruling class in control of Ireland from 17th to 19th centuries

1	
2	
3	
4	
5	
6	

2 Explain the following terms in relation to **Plantations in Ireland.** (Literacy)

Common law	
Plantation towns	
Irish Society	
Crown land	
Church land	
Central diamond	
'Loyal Irish'	
Penal laws	
'To hell or to Connacht'	
Down Survey	
Adventurers (1)	
Adventurers (2)	
Transplanted	
Sectarian	

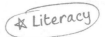

3 Put these events in relation to the **Plantations in Ireland** in chronological order.

Historical skills   Numeracy

Events		Dates	Order
A	The Act of Settlement was passed		
B	The native Irish attacked the planters in a rebellion and massacred thousands of them		
C	The land was divided into estates of 1,000, 1,500 and 2,000 acres		
D	The beginning of the Nine Years War		
E	The Desmond Rebellions		
F	Henry VII introduced a policy of surrender and regrant		
G	O'Neill and O'Donnell were defeated at the Battle of Kinsale		
H	The walls of Derry/Londonderry were completed		
I	Maryborough was founded		
J	The land was divided into estates of 4,000, 6,000, 8,000 and 12,000 acres		
K	O'Neill and other chiefs fled Ireland in the Flight of the Earls		
L	The private plantation of Montgomery and Hamilton		

4 Fill in the blank spaces on the Results of the **Plantation of Ulster** from the word list below.

Word List: Plantation towns; Farmers & labourers; 1641 Rebellion; Farming methods change; Church of England; Loyal population; Land & religious differences; The Troubles; 40,000 in 1641; Central diamond; western Ulster; Straight, wide streets; Presbyterians; Nationalists & Unionists; English common law; Business & trade; Coleraine & Londonderry; Further immigration from Scotland; Partition.

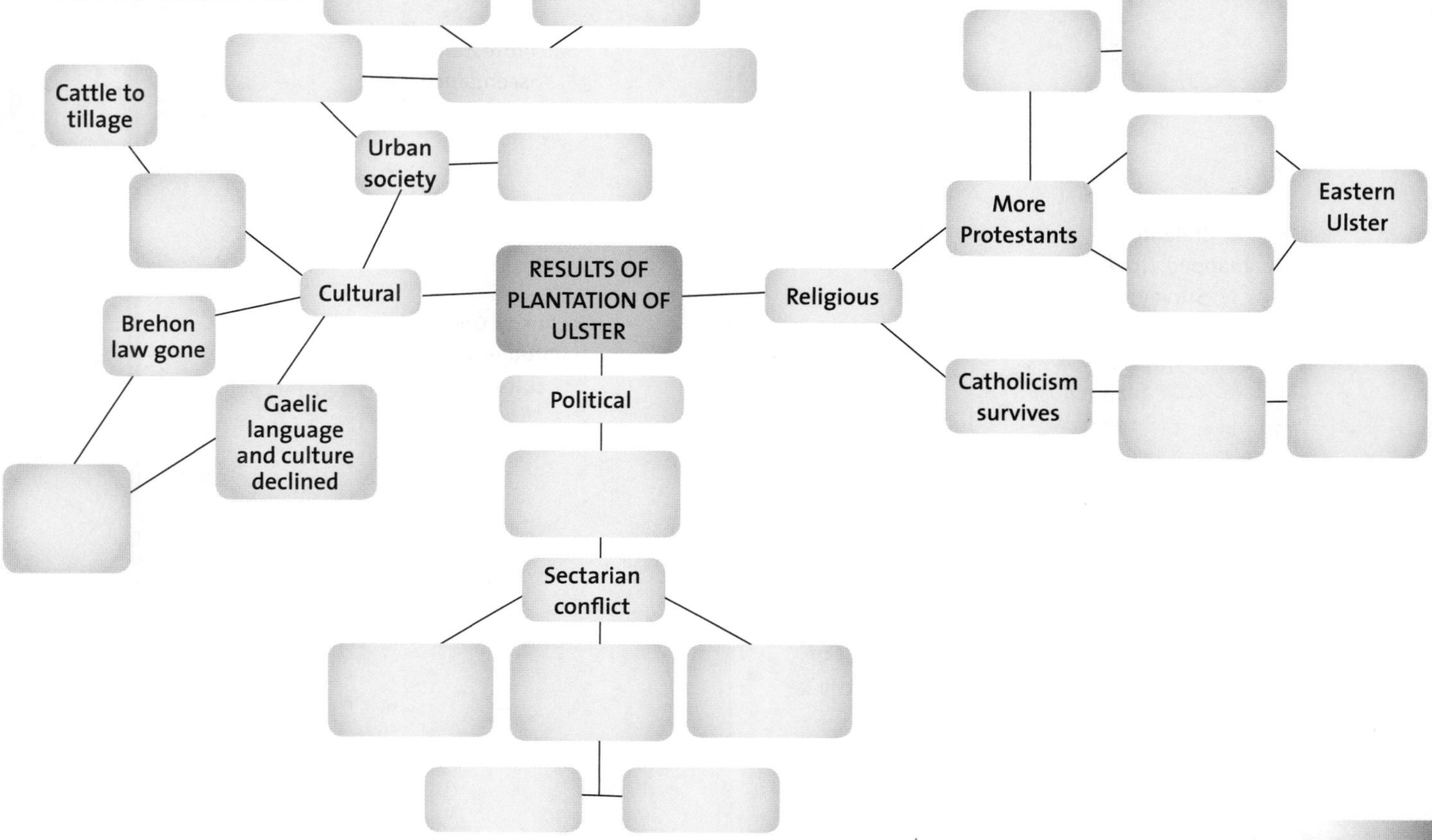

❺ Fill in the blank boxes on the **Impact of the Plantations** from the word list below. *Historical skills*

Word List: Presbyterians & Church of England; Penal laws; Catholic tenants & labourers; The Troubles; Protestant minority in the south; New farming methods; 19th-century Land War; Loyal Protestant population; 1641 Massacre; Sectarian conflict in Northern Ireland; English common law; Regular field patterns; Killarney & Coleraine; Increased trade.

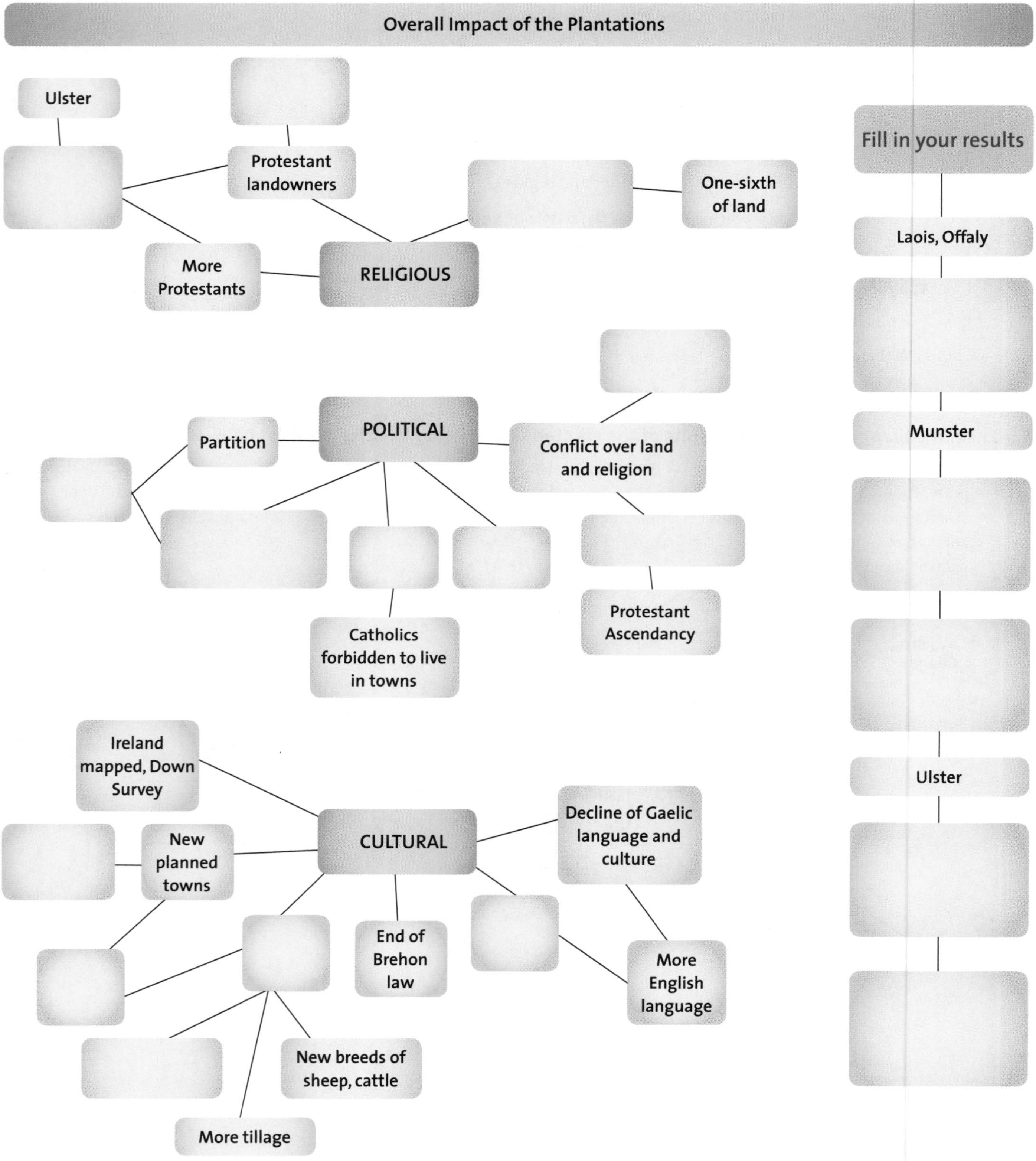

14 The American War of Independence

Key ideas

Causes – British rule of America, thirteen colonies; Navigation Acts; Seven Years War – more taxation; Stamp Act – no taxation without representation; tax on tea; Boston Massacre, Boston Tea Party; Intolerable Acts; arms in Lexington and Concord – first shots of War of Independence, Paul Revere; Tom Paine's *Common Sense*.

George Washington – Mount Vernon – tobacco plantation; fought in Seven Years War; Virginia delegate to Continental Congress; commander-in-chief of Continental (American) army; supported Declaration of Independence; problems with army – part-time; success at Boston, defeat at New York; success at Trenton, Princeton; Battle of Saratoga – turning point in war – French help; winter in Valley Forge, von Steuben; defeated Cornwallis at Yorktown; Treaty of Versailles – American independence; Constitutional Convention – American Constitution; president – eight years; died, buried at Mount Vernon; Father of the United States.

Results – USA founded, now most powerful country; ideas of Declaration of Independence followed elsewhere; example to French people; encouraged move for greater independence for Irish parliament.

1 Fill in the blank spaces in the **Causes of the American War of Independence**.

Relations between the American colonies and Britain got worse during the e_____________ century.

The N_____________ Acts stated that some American products, such as sugar, cotton and tobacco, could be sold only to England.

These acts led to widespread s_____________ by the Americans, which led to clashes with the English.

After the Seven Years War, the British insisted that the Americans must be t_____________ to cover the cost of fighting the war.

The British government passed the S_____________ Act. Americans had to have n_____________ and legal documents stamped by government officials.

S_____________ were burned and stamp officials were attacked.

Americans used the slogan, 'No t_____________ without r_____________'. This became the slogan of the Sons of L_____________.

Britain imposed taxes on a number of imported goods, including t_____________.

When an angry crowd stoned British troops, the soldiers opened fire and killed five people in the Boston M_____________.

Americans disguised as Indians dumped 342 crates of tea from British ships into Boston

Harbour in the Boston T____________ P____________.

This resulted in the British government imposing the 'I____________ Acts' on Boston and the colony of Massachusetts.

Paul Revere rode his horse through the night to warn people that British troops were marching towards L____________ and C____________

Tom Paine wrote *Common Sense* in which he said that America should fight for complete i____________ from Britain.

❷ Which of these statements in relation to **George Washington** are true and which are false? Tick the correct answer.

	True	False
George Washington owned a cotton plantation called Mount Vernon.		
He fought in the Seven Years War against the British.		
George Washington represented Massachusetts at the Continental Congress in Philadelphia.		
He was appointed commander-in-chief of the Continental army.		
The Continental Congress passed the Declaration of Independence on 4 July 1776.		
The Continental Army was largely made up of part-time Indian fighters.		
The Americans used guerrilla tactics.		
The British had a professional (full-time) army and navy and four times more soldiers.		
Washington began with some success when he forced the British out of Chicago.		
He ordered an invasion of British-controlled Canada but this plan failed.		
He was defeated in New York in the Battle of Long Island.		
Washington attacked the British army at Trenton but lost.		
Washington next surprised the British at Princeton and won.		
The American general Horatio Gates forced a large British army to surrender at the Battle of Saratoga.		
Washington had to retreat to Valley Forge during the winter of 1777–78		
His soldiers were well trained by a German officer, von Steuben.		
In the Battle of Yorktown, Cornwallis, the British commander, was surrounded by Washington's forces on land and by a French fleet from the sea.		
Cornwallis fought his way out.		

	True	False
Peace was made at the Treaty of Paris.		
Washington became President of the Constitutional Convention in Philadelphia.		
Washington was elected as the first President of the United States of America.		
He became known as the Father of America.		

3 Causes of the American War of Independence – Using Key Ideas (Historical skills) (Communication)

Write your own account of the causes of the **American War of Independence** using the words under Causes, p. 61, without referring to your textbook.

Make each point and develop it

4 Focus Task (IT)

Create a **Fakebook page** for **George Washington** at www.classtools.net/**FAKEBOOK**

Use information from your textbook and from George Washington, www.mountvernon.org/george-washington/

15 The French Revolution

Key ideas

Causes – France an absolute monarchy – King Louis XVI held absolute power, wife Marie Antoinette not liked, criticism by French thinkers, Age of Enlightenment – wanted limited power; privileges of clergy (First Estate), nobility (Second Estate) – paid no taxes, Third Estate paid taxes; American War of Independence – cost, need for more taxes; meeting of Estates-General – conflict over voting, Tennis Court Oath, formation of Constituent Assembly.

Progress – fall of Bastille, Constituent Assembly abolishes privileges of nobles, tithes, Declaration of the Rights of Man; slogan of revolution – Liberty, Equality, Fraternity; women of Paris bring king to Paris; king caught at Varennes; war against Austria, Prussia; king jailed, executed for plotting with Austria.

Robespierre and Reign of Terror – lawyer, supported ideas of revolution, voted for execution of king, known as 'Incorruptible', member of Jacobins, Committee of Public Safety; Law of Suspects, Reign of Terror, guillotine, stopped rebellion; huge army defeated enemies; Law of Maximum to control prices; enemies – he was arrested, tried, executed along with supporters; end of French Revolution.

Results – rise of Napoleon; spread of ideas of Liberty, Equality, Fraternity; influence on Ireland, United Irishmen, 1798 Rebellion; abolition of slavery; rise of middle classes, loss of power by nobility; metric system.

1 Fill in the blank spaces about **Robespierre and the Reign of Terror** using information from the word list below.

Word List: Jacobin; invasion; Convention; monarchy; enemies; Public; republic; democratic; lawyer; disorder; conspiracy; autocracy; guillotine; Paris; supported; cult; Estates-General; Reign; Rousseau; Assembly; treason; mob.

Robespierre was a French ______________ and politician who became one of the most influential figures of the French Revolution.

Maximilien Robespierre was born in Arras on 6 May 1758, the son of a lawyer. He was educated in Paris and entered the same profession as his father. He was elected a deputy of the ______________-______________ (a form of parliament, but without real power) that met in May 1789, and subsequently served in the National Constituent ______________. Robespierre became increasingly popular for his attacks on the ______________ and his advocacy of ______________ reforms. In April 1790, he was elected president of the powerful ______________ political club. After the downfall of the monarchy in August 1792, Robespierre was elected first deputy for ______________ to the National Convention. The convention abolished the monarchy, declared France a ______________ and put the king on trial for ______________, all measures strongly ______________ by Robespierre. The king was executed in January 1793.

In the period after the king's execution, tensions in the convention resulted in a power struggle between the Jacobins and the more moderate Girondins. The Jacobins used the power of the ______________ to take control and the Girondin leaders were arrested. Control of the country passed to the Committee of ______________ Safety, of which Robespierre was a member. He rapidly became the dominant force on the committee.

Against a backdrop of the threat of foreign ____________ and increasing ____________ in the country, the committee began the '____________ of Terror', ruthlessly eliminating all those considered ____________ of the revolution. These included leading revolutionary figures such as Georges Danton.

In May 1794, Robespierre insisted that the National ____________ proclaim a new official religion for France – the ____________ of the Supreme Being. This was based on the thinking of the philosopher Jean-Jacques ____________, of whom Robespierre was a passionate advocate (supporter/promoter).

The intensification of the '____________ of Terror' and Robespierre's ____________ (tyranny/dictatorship) made him increasingly unpopular. French military successes served to undermine the justification (reason) for such ruthlessness and a ____________ was formed to overthrow Robespierre. On 27 July 1794, he was arrested after a struggle. The following day Robespierre, wounded from a bullet to the jaw, and 21 of his closest supporters were executed at the ____________.

2 Which of the following statements are **causes or results/effects** of the French Revolution? Tick the correct column in each.

Historical skills

	Causes	Effects/results
The American War of Independence bankrupted France.		
The peasants propped up the nobility and the clergy.		
The Estates-General met to discuss new taxes.		
Many French thinkers were part of the Age of Enlightenment.		
Napoleon rose to power.		
War broke out between France and other European countries.		
Lafayette fought in America.		
There were massacres in some cities in France.		
French revolutionary ideas spread across Europe.		
Wolfe Tone got help from France.		
The American example was followed by other countries.		
The sans-culottes rose to power.		
Robespierre was guillotined.		

16 Ireland in the Age of Revolutions

Key ideas

Causes – Protestant Ascendancy – parliament, laws, controlled by members of Church of Ireland (Anglican), only 15% of population; Catholic and Presbyterian discontent – penal laws used to discriminate against Catholics (75%) and Presbyterians (10%). Influence of American Revolution – defeated Britain, gained independence. Influence of French Revolution – principles of liberty, equality, fraternity, fall of Bastille celebrated in Dublin and Belfast. Poverty – rapid rise in population, subdivision of farms, people paid high rents and tithes, agrarian societies (Ribbonmen).

Wolfe Tone and United Irishmen (1) – Tone born in Dublin, Anglican family, lawyer, more interested in politics; admired principles of French Revolution, wanted reforms for Catholics; invited to Belfast, Society of United Irishmen (UI) founded, aims – reform parliament, fair deal for all religions, end English control of Irish affairs; Tone disappointed with reforms won by Catholic Committee for Catholics (e.g. still could not become MPs), Tone helped French spy (William Jackson) – caught, had to go to America; then went to France to get help for Ireland; came with French fleet to Bantry Bay, could not land, storm.

Rising of 1798 – Government action – death for administering oaths, wide powers of search, arrest, punishment, General Lake used torture and flogging in Ulster and Leinster, arrest of leaders of UI, including Lord Edward Fitzgerald, wounded, died. The Rising – four main areas; around Dublin, mail coaches. Wexford – Fr Murphy, Bagenal Harvey (Protestant landlord), defeated yeomanry and militia at Oulart Hll, captured Enniscorthy, Wexford, burned barn at Scullabogue (200 Protestants killed), defeated at New Ross, Arklow and Vinegar Hill. Ulster – Henry Joy McCracken in Co. Antrim, Henry Munro in Co. Down, both defeated, executed. Connacht – French General Humbert landed at Killala, Co. Mayo, defeated British at the Races of Castlebar, Humbert defeated in Ballinamuck, Co. Longford. Reasons for failure of Rising – poor organisation, spies, stronger British force, insufficient French help.

Wolfe Tone (2) – Tone got French government to send more troops, fleet with 3,000 soldiers; captured off Donegal, including Tone; sent to Dublin, tried, guilty of treason, committed suicide rather than be executed.

Results of Rising – 300,000 people died; bitterness between Catholics and Protestants; Act of Union passed, parliament in Dublin abolished; rule from Westminster. Rebellion of 1803 – badly organised by Robert Emmett, few incidents in Dublin, Emmett arrested, tried and executed. Tone – Father of Irish Republicanism, Britain never-ending source of Ireland's troubles, create Irish republic, inspired later revolutions, including 1916 Rising.

Overall results of Age of Revolutions – power of monarchy reduced; growth of democracy; greater equality of people; more independence, e.g. America; use of physical force (revolution) widespread; growth of armies (conscripted).

1 Which of the following statements in relation to **Wolfe Tone** are true and which are false? Tick the appropriate boxes.

Statement	True	False
He was educated as a lawyer.		
He admired the ideas of the French Revolution.		
He went to England on a delegation to present a petition of Catholic grievances.		
He wrote a report on conditions in Ireland for Fr Murphy, a French spy.		
He landed in Bantry Bay but had to return to France.		
He went to Killala with General Humbert.		
He was captured in Lough Derg.		
He was tried for forgery.		
He was shot by firing squad.		

2 Chronology of the Age of Revolutions

Numeracy

Research the year of each of the following events relating to **the Age of Revolutions**, and insert the **dates** in the blank boxes. Number the events chronologically and then insert the number for each event (1 (earliest) to 10) along the timeline below at the appropriate place.

	Events	Dates	Order
1	Boston Tea Party		
2	Founding of United Irishmen		
3	Fall of Bastille		
4	Reign of Terror		
5	Rising in Wexford		
6	Declaration of Independence		
7	French invasion fleet in Bantry Bay		
8	Wolfe Tone captured		
9	Battle of Yorktown		
10	Act of Union		

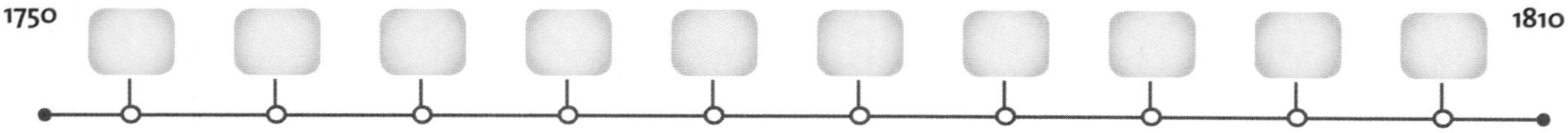

3 **Reasons for the failure of the 1798 Rebellion in Ireland – Mind Map**

Use your textbook and the Internet to develop a mind map on the reasons for the failure of the 1798 Rebellion in Ireland (see p. 203).

REASONS FOR FAILURE OF 1798 REBELLION

Revising the Age of Revolutions

Literacy

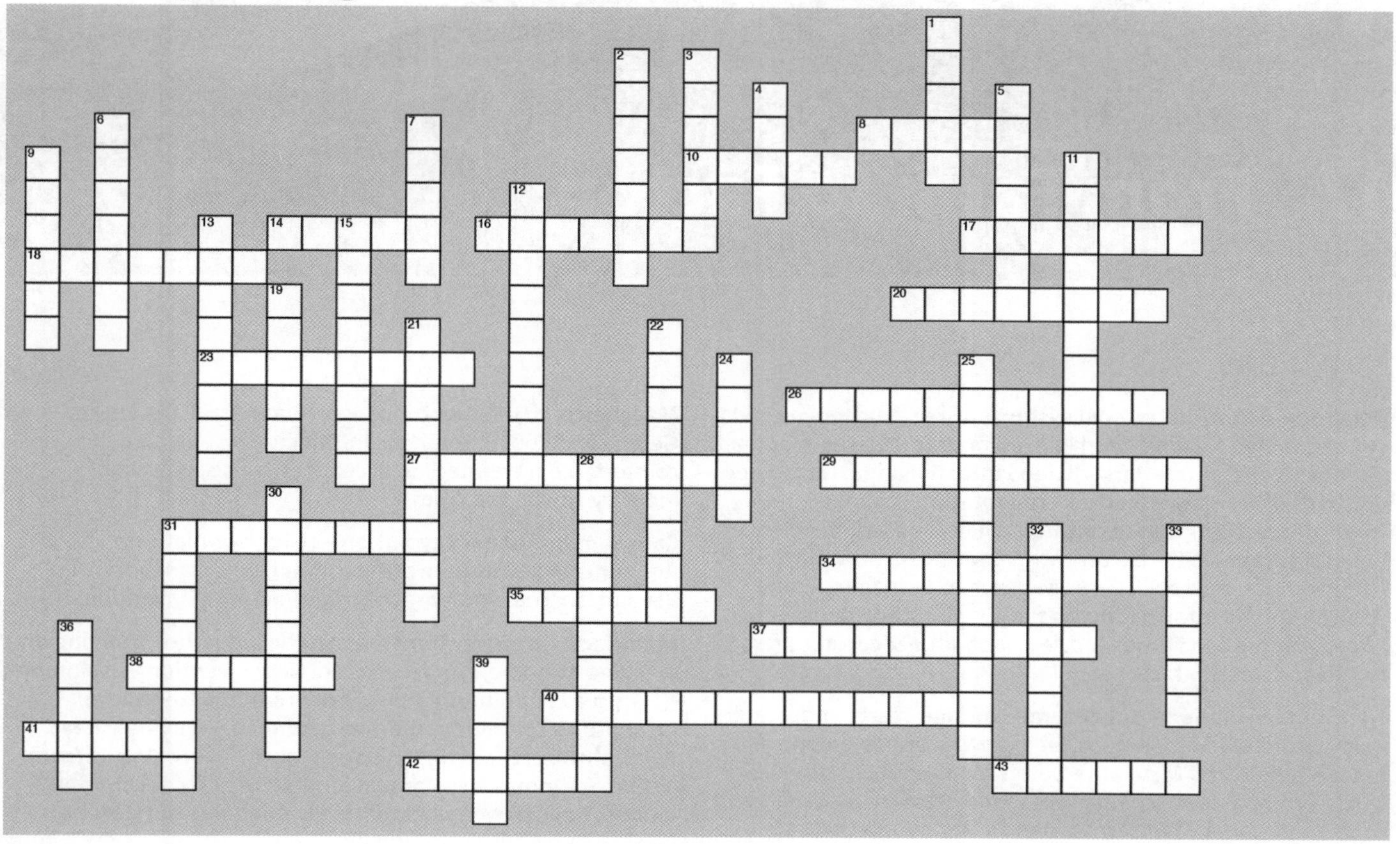

ACROSS

8 Wrote *Common Sense*.

10 Laws against Catholics and Presbyterians in 18th-century Ireland.

14 One-tenth of crops paid to support the church

16 With Equality and Fraternity.

17 Law to control prices in Reign of Terror.

18 Victory for Washington at Christmas.

20 Prison in Paris, sparked the French Revolution.

23 The number of colonies in America in the 18th century.

26 Defeat for the rebels in Wexford in 1798.

27 British commander at Yorktown.

29 Organised the Reign of Terror.

31 A turning point in the American War of Independence.

34 Massacre of Protestants in Wexford.

35 Failed landing of Hoche's fleet.

37 Acts controlling American trade.

38 French system of weights and measurements.

40 The nickname for Robespierre.

41 Rising in 1803.

42 Tone captured here.

43 Rode through the night warning people.

DOWN

1 Treaty which ended the war between America and Britain.

2 Arms held there by American revolutionaries.

3 Priest who led rebellion in Wexford in 1798.

4 Father of Irish Republicanism.

5 Where United Irishmen were founded.

6 French general in Killala.

7 Went from Paris to Versailles to bring the King to Paris.

9 Massacre and Tea Party.

11 Instrument for executing people in France.

12 Agrarian societies in 18th-century Ireland.

13 Final surrender of the British to Washington.

15 Won't pay without representation.

19 Act abolishing parliament in Dublin.

21 Greater say for people in running government.

22 Races and defeat of the British.

24 The Estate of the clergy in France.

25 Working-class revolutionaries in Paris.

28 Protestant control in 18th-century Ireland.

30 Political group in France in the Revolution.

31 Law against opponents of French Revolution.

32 Style of monarchy in 18th-century France.

33 Also called Age of Enlightenment.

36 Act to pay taxes on newspapers in America.

39 The name of the King of France.

17 From Farm to Factory

Key ideas

Agricultural Revolution – old system – three-field, open-field system; faults, e.g. one-third idle, no machinery, weeds spread. Changes – enclosure – land divided into individual farms; new methods of farming – Norfolk crop rotation (Charles Townshend), turnips to feed cattle, all fields used; selective breeding (Bakewell) – better cattle and sheep; new machinery – Jethro Tull – seed drill; Cyrus McCormack – reaper; Arthur Young – spread information on farming improvements. Effects – more food produced, less labour needed, labourers could work in new factories.

Transport Revolution – old system – carriages, carts, ships; faults – slow, expensive, small loads, breakdowns. Improvements – roads – Telford and McAdam – better road surfaces; turnpike trusts – companies to charge tolls to maintain roads. Canals and ships – first canal – Worsley to Manchester, owner Duke of Bridgewater, engineer James Brindley, aqueduct, transport coal; ships – steam engines instead of sail. Railways – railroads to haul coal from coal mines; Richard Trevethick – first train; Stockton to Darlington – first goods train – George Stephenson; Manchester to Liverpool – first passenger train, the Rocket – George and Robert Stephenson. Effects – faster, more comfortable travel, decline of coaches, canals; growth of industry, towns and cities.

Causes of Industrial Revolution – rising population; Agricultural Revolution; profits from trade; Transport Revolution; coal and iron ore; manufacturing inventions.

Manufacturing inventions – domestic industry – spinning and weaving at home, hand-powered. New inventions – spinning – Hargreave's Spinning Jenny, Arkwright's water frame, Crompton's spinning mule – more thread. Weaving – Kay's flying shuttle, Cartwright's power loom – more cloth. Steam engine – Thomas Newcomen, James Watt – flywheel, rotary motion, could power other machines. Coal, iron and steel – coal for steam power, coke for smelting iron ore, chemicals, dyes; iron and steel – charcoal replaced by coke, Abraham Darby; iron replaced timber; steel – Henry Bessemer. Result – change from domestic system to factory system.

1 Explain these Key Terms in relation to the **Industrial and Agricultural Revolutions.** (☆ Literacy)

Domestic system	
Enclosure	
Norfolk crop rotation	

2 Planning and writing a People in History answer. (☆ Communication)

A farm labourer during the Agricultural Revolution

This question is on a farm labourer during the Agricultural Revolution, so you must concentrate on this.

Go through your textbook and your notes and list key points about the farm labourer on which you can base your answer. Even though little is directly said about farm labourers, you can base your answer on the farming systems and changes at that time.

Some key points could be:

- Commenting on the old farming system
- Enclosure

Add some more here:

Take each of the key points and add historical information about it. For example:

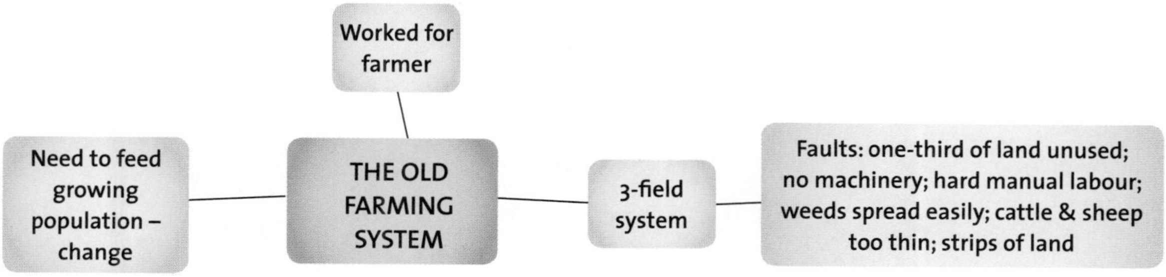

When you are satisfied with that, move on to each of the next points and add historical information. Once you have each of the points filled in, you can write up your answer.

Writing the answer

I was a farm labourer during the Agricultural Revolution, working for a farmer. I didn't like the old system he used, which was called the open field or three-field system. It had many faults – I had to do hard manual labour because there was no machinery. One-third of the land was unused, weeds spread easily and cattle and sheep were too thin. So the farmer and the whole village had to change the system, which they did with enclosure, to feed a growing population. Now the farmer has his own farm in one piece, not like before when it was scattered into strips. Now there is machinery, which is a great help to me.

You can use this system to plan and write other People in History answers.

3 Match the item in Column A with the corresponding name in Column B.

Literacy

Column A		Column B	
1	Seed drill	A	George and Robert Stephenson
2	Worsley to Manchester canal	B	Abraham Darby
3	The Rocket	C	James Brindley
4	First steam engine on wheels	D	James Hargreaves
5	Spinning Jenny	E	Edmund Cartwright
6	Flying shuttle	F	Jethro Tull
7	Power loom	G	James Kay
8	Rotary motion in steam engine	H	Richard Trevethick
9	Safety lamp	I	Humphrey Davy
10	Coke for smelting iron ore	J	Robert Bakewell
11	Selective breeding	K	James Watt

1	
2	
3	
4	
5	
6	
7	
8	
9	
10	
11	

4 **The Transport Revolution – Using Key Ideas**

Write your own account of the **Transport Revolution** using the words under **Transport Revolution**, on p. 70, without referring to your textbook.

Make each point and develop it

18 Special Study – Contrasting Lifestyles *c.* 1859: Industrial England and Rural Ireland

Key ideas

Working in factories – three to five storeys tall, small windows, deafening noise, hot and moist conditions, dusty; work 15 hours a day, low pay – men 80p a week, women less than half men's pay, children half women's pay; workers fined for breaking rules – late for work, whistling, singing, opening window; children beaten, danger from accidents – children under machinery, women's clothes, hair caught in machines, bad injuries or death; employers wanted to make profit.

Working in the mines – children of age 5 – trappers – open and close trapdoors, cold and damp, 12 hours' work a day, scared of dark; older boys and girls carried coal – hurriers – large baskets, filled wagons; women pulled wagons, worked even when pregnant; accidents common – falling down shafts, falling stones, gas explosions, miner's lung – disease from inhaling coal dust; danger of flooding; Davy safety lamp to prevent explosions.

Living conditions in the cities – urbanisation – growth of cities – London, Manchester, Liverpool – why? More births, migration from countryside, immigration from Ireland; cities grew without a plan around factories. Houses – in slums (rundown areas) – cellars flooded, built back to back, leaking roofs, damp walls, no indoor toilets or piped water; outdoor toilet and pump in street; open drains, polluted water; families in one room, little or no furniture, rats, disease spread – cholera (dirty water), typhus (insects), TB (damp rooms) – London 50,000 died from cholera, 1848–49; labourers died younger than middle class; rich better off, comfortable lives. Health – hospitals – dangerous, many died from operations, great pain; **improvements** – James Simpson – chloroform for anaesthetic, women in childbirth; James Lister – dirt and disease, insisted on cleanliness, cleaner operating theatres; Edward Jenner – vaccinated with cowpox to prevent smallpox. Improvements in living conditions – government reports ('Blue Books') showed how bad conditions were; trade unions pressed for reforms; individual factory owners, e.g. Robert Owen, individual politicians, e.g. Earl of Shaftsbury; **Factory and Mines Acts** – reduced hours of work, some schooling, inspectors appointed to enforce laws. Public health – Edwin Chadwick wrote *The Sanitary Condition of the Labouring Population* – conditions in cities – led to Public Health Act 1848 – streets paved, cleaned, inspection of houses, better houses, sewerage pipes, water supplies, slum clearance.

Rich and poor – food – poor close to starvation level; rich plentiful supply of fish, beef, etc. Clothes – poor had very few clothes, dirty; rich – colourful and elaborate clothes. Education – working-class children did not go to school, worked, some went to Sunday School – Bible education – more education after Factory Acts; rich sons – private tutors, public schools (Eton, Harrow). Leisure – working class, very little time for leisure, free time in pubs – Gin Alley; Factory Acts and half-day Saturday – more free time; skilled workers and middle class – trains, day trips to seaside, growth of organised sport – soccer, racing, cricket, rugby.

❶ Match the item in Column A with the corresponding name in Column B. (✯ Literacy)

Column A		Column B	
1	Flooding in mines	A	James Simpson
2	Explosive and poisonous gases in mines	B	Robert Owen
3	Shocking conditions in the mines	C	Edward Jenner
4	Chloroform as anaesthetic	D	Newcomen's steam engine
5	Dirt and disease	E	Edwin Chadwick
6	Clean streets, piped water	F	Joseph Lister
7	Vaccination	G	Ventilation shafts and trapdoors
8	New Lanark factory	H	1833 Factory Act
9	*The Sanitary Condition of the Labouring Population*	I	Boards of Health
10	Inspectors appointed to enforce the law	J	Mines Report

1	
2	
3	
4	
5	
6	
7	
8	
9	
10	

❷ How useful and reliable are the following sources on conditions in the mines?

SOURCE ANALYSIS: DOCUMENTS

Source A

The tunnels are sometimes of great length. In the Booth Town Pit, I walked and crept 1800 yards to one of the nearest faces. The door of this gate was every here and there three or four inches deep in water and muddy throughout. The Swan Bank Pit was almost as bad and more resembled a city drain than anything else.

The roofs and the walls are at some places even, at others rough, rocky and loose, needing proppings (wooden supports) to support them: despite, however, every care, large masses sometimes fall burying the children.

Children's Employment Commission, 1842

Source B

I'm a trapper* in the pit. It does not tire me, but I have to trap without a light and I'm scared. I go at four and sometimes half past three in the morning, and come out at five and half past. I never go to sleep. Sometimes I sing when I've light, but not in the dark; I dare not sing then. I don't like being in the pit. I am very sleepy when I go sometimes in the morning.

I go to Sunday-schools and read *Reading made Easy*. I have heard tell of Jesus many a time. I don't know why he came on earth, I'm sure, and I don't know why he died. I would like to be at school far better than in the pit.

Sarah Gooder (aged 8) from Children's Employment Commission Report, 1842

Source C

We have but one girl working with us, by name Ann Ambler, gets 6/- [30p] a week. She hurries* by herself and has to carry the same weight and distance as I have; there is not a bit of difference between any of us. I have seen her thrashed many times when she does not please: they rap her in the face and knock her down. She does not like the work. I have seen her cry many times.

Report from Children's Employment Commission, 1842

**Trapper*: child who opened and closed air venting door to allow carts through

**Hurrier*: child or woman who transported coal in mines

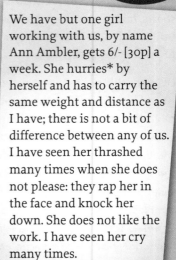

(i) Source A: ______________________________

____

(ii) Source B: ______________________________

____

(iii) Source C: ______________________________

____

❸ Fill in the blank spaces in this account of **housing in the Industrial Revolution** from the word list below (some words may be used more than once).

Word List: profit; cheap; Liverpool; stench; cesspits; garden; terraces; bathroom; toilet; night; cholera; courtyard; damp; back; cellar; regulations; hygiene.

The Industrial Revolution witnessed a huge growth in the size of British cities. These cities were not prepared for such an influx in such a short period of time and cities such as Birmingham, L____________, Manchester, etc. suffered problems not witnessed anywhere else in the world at this time.

These cities needed c____________ homes as the Industrial Revolution continued to grow. There were few building r____________ then and those that did exist were frequently ignored. P____________ became the main motivator for builders. They knew that those coming to the cities needed a job and somewhere to live. Therefore, a house was put up quickly and cheaply – and as many were built as was possible. The Industrial Revolution saw the start of what were known as b____________-to-b____________ terrace housing. These had no g____________ and the only part of the building not connected to another house would be the front (and only) entrance.

The building material used was the cheapest a builder could find. The finished homes were d____________. as none were built with damp courses and those who could only afford c____________ dwellings lived in the worst possible conditions as damp and moisture would seep to the lowest part of the house.

None of these homes was built with a b____________, t____________ or running water. You either washed in a tin bath in the home with the water being collected from a local pump or you simply did not wash.

There would be a c____________ between each row of t____________. Waste of all sorts from the homes was thrown into the courtyard and so-called n____________-men would collect this at night and dispose of it. Sanitation and h____________ barely existed and throughout the 18th and 19th centuries the great fear was a c____________, typhus or typhoid epidemic.

Toilets would have been nothing more than c____________. When these were filled they had to be emptied and what was collected was loaded onto a cart before being dumped in a local river. This work was also done by the n____________-men. Local laws stated that their work had to be done at night as the s____________ created by emptying the c____________ was too great to be tolerated during the day.

(*Source*: 'Life in Industrial Towns', www.HistoryLearningSite.co.uk, 2008)

19 Special Study – Rural Ireland in the 1840s

Key ideas

Population – rapid growth, to 8.2 million in 1841, most lived in countryside, Dublin, Cork, Belfast only sizeable cities; Belfast only industrial city.

Landlords – 20,000 landlords (owned and rented land to tenants), descended from planters, mostly Protestant; large and smaller estates; some absentee (living in Dublin or England); lived in 'Big House', employed servants; rent collected by landlord's agent; tenants often evicted, mostly for non-payment of rent. **Tenant farmers** – rented land from landlords. **Large farmers** – over 30 acres, wheat, barley, cattle, pigs; hired labourers; two-storey house, slated or thatched – kitchen, parlour, bedrooms; well-fed – vegetables, meat, potatoes; sons educated, arranged marriages for daughters, with dowry. **Small farmers** – 5 to 15 acres, thatched cottages; crops to pay rent, food mostly potatoes, some milk, bread, bacon and fish now and again. **Cottiers** – labourers who rented up to 1 acre from farmers – worked on farm to pay off rent; one-roomed cabins, damp, no windows, little furniture, slept on straw, earthen floor; depended on potatoes for food. **Landless labourers** – very badly off, no work in winter, mud cabins on the edge of towns, lived on potatoes and milk, herrings occasionally. Spailpeens – wandering labourers – young unmarried men and women, travelled around looking for work; hired in spring or harvest time, at hiring fairs; lived in farmer's house.

Poverty – increased poverty – why? Growing population, failed harvests, dependence on farming; 70% of families had very little food; some emigrated to England, better-off paid £3 to £5 to emigrate to USA or Canada (130,000 in 1841); poor in Ireland went to workhouse – each Poor Law Union (district) had a workhouse – families split up, conditions bad to discourage people going there.

The Great Famine (or Hunger) from 1845 to 1850 – Causes: Rise in population – 8.2 million in 1841, some areas more densely populated than others; people made poorer, especially labourers, cottiers, small farmers. Subdivision – only industry was in Belfast, people depended on farming, more subdivision of land because of rising population – smaller farms so people poorer. Dependence on potato – poorer families dependent on potato – three meals of potatoes a day – only food for 4 million people. The blight – disease rotted potatoes, those dependent on potatoes had no other food, so starvation, famine.

Progress of famine – blight came from America – only affected some areas in 1845; entire crop destroyed in 1846 – widespread starvation; blight less severe in 1847 but fewer seed potatoes so smaller crop – more starvation; blight very bad again in 1848 – two-thirds of crop destroyed; blight struck again in 1849 and 1850 but worst of famine was over.

Help for famine victims – Government response – Indian corn – bought by government of Robert Peel in 1845, £100,000 worth, fed 1 million, sold through government depots, lessened impact of the famine; Peel also set up public works for poor people to earn money building roads, piers. **Laissez-faire** – new Prime Minister, Lord John Russell – believed that government interference would make economy worse; stopped policy of buying corn; more public works – ¾ million employed – problems? Low pay, workers too weak to work, had to walk long distances to work. Soup kitchens – first organised by **Society of Friends** (Quakers) – soup given to poor; Soup Kitchen Act – government set up soup kitchens – 3 million being fed in 1847; then closed down – help to be given through workhouses instead. **Workhouses** – 200,000 people there – overcrowded, conditions bad, disease spread; soup kitchens when workhouses were full – 800,000 helped this way.

Disease – more people died from disease than from starvation – typhus, yellow fever – spread by body lice in overcrowded workhouses and towns; affected rich and poor.

Emigration – to Britain, USA, Canada – 250,000 to USA in 1847, 200,000 emigrate for each of next five years; helped by landlords; helped by family members; whole families left; some ships unsuitable for Atlantic voyages – 'coffin ships' – passengers packed in, disease spread, very little food, many died.

Results of famine – Fall in population – fell 2 million – 1 million from hunger and disease, 1 million from emigration; cottiers, labourers worst hit; western seaboard worst hit; population decline, emigration continued after the famine. Subdivision ended – eldest son got land, other sons and daughters remained single or emigrated; eldest son married late – decline in population. Decline in Irish language – Irish-speaking areas worst hit by death and emigration; decline continued after famine. Politics – English government blamed for famine – emigrants took hatred of England abroad to USA – later supported Fenians, Land League, 1916 Rising, IRA.

1 Which of the following statements about **Rural Ireland in the 1840s** are true and which are false? Tick the appropriate boxes.

Statement	True	False
By 1841, there were 10 million people living in Ireland.		
Only three cities had populations of more than 100,000 – Dublin, Cork and Belfast.		
Landlords rented the land to tenant farmers.		
There were about 50,000 landlords in Ireland.		
The rent was collected twice a year by the landlord's agent.		
Middlemen rented land from bigger landlords.		
Large farmers hired labourers to help with farm work and servants to help with housework.		
The small farmers rented between 50 and 150 acres of land.		
Cottiers used a system of conacre.		
Cottiers were landless labourers.		
Spailpeens lived in the Big Houses of the landlords.		
The country was divided into 130 districts called Poor Law Divisions.		

2 Fill in the blank spaces on the **Causes of the Great Famine** from the statements below. Historical skills

Statements: Some areas were densely populated; People depended on farming; Those who lived on potatoes had no food; Potatoes could be grown on poor land; Smaller farms resulted in poorer people; Labourers, cottiers and small farmers were very poor; The disease hit Ireland in the autumn of 1845; Industry had not developed except around Belfast; For about 4 million people, the potato was the only food; As the population increased the people got poorer; Potatoes were very nutritious; Population increase resulted in subdivision of the land

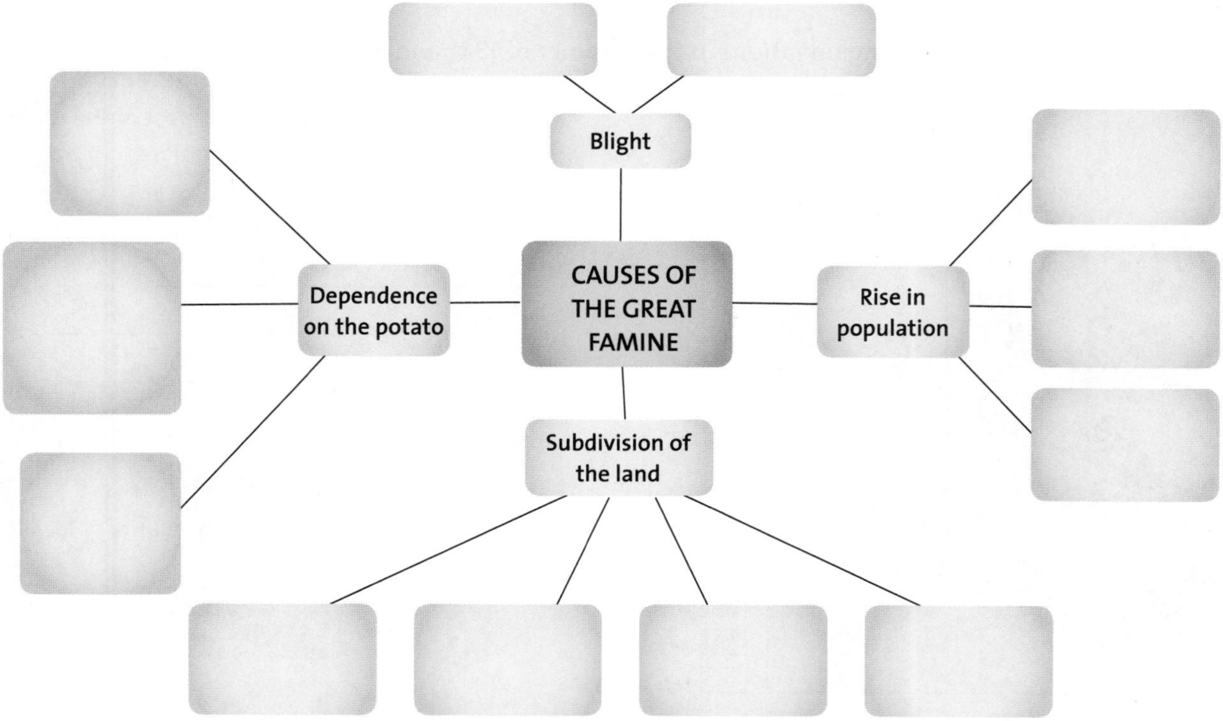

❸ Construct a graph showing the tonnage of potatoes produced in Ireland from 1844 to 1849. Use www.chartgo.com to construct your graph.

How do these figures explain how a famine occurred in Ireland at this time?

✩ Numeracy ✩ IT

1844	15 million tons
1845	10 million tons
1846	3 million tons
1847	2 million tons
1848	3 million tons
1849	4 million tons
1850	4.25 million tons

❹ Explain the following terms in relation to the **Progress of the Famine.** ✩ Literacy

Laissez-faire	
Peel's Brimstone	
Society of Friends	
Soup kitchens	
Workhouses	
Coffin ships	

❺ Study the map of percentage taking up rations in the summer of 1847 and answer the questions. ✩ Numeracy

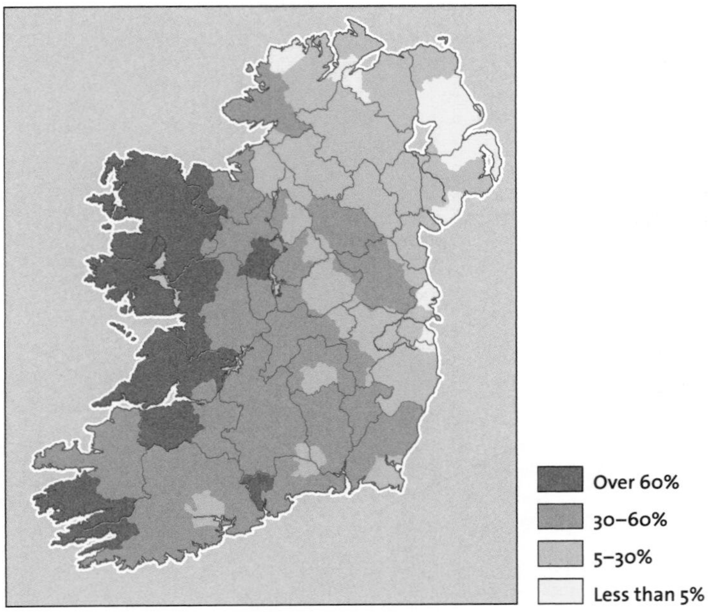

List the counties where some or most of the country had over 60% of the people on rations in 1847.

What was the percentage in your county or locality?

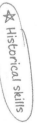

6 Fill in the blank spaces on the **Results of the Great Famine** from the statements below. Historical skills

Statements: Eldest son got the land; Irish diaspora created; 1 million died from disease; Due to death and emigration from Irish-speaking areas; Emigrants took hatred of Britain to USA; Eldest son married late; Emigration continued after the famine; Western countries worst hit; Continued after the famine; Younger sons and daughters forced to emigrate; Larger farms; 1 million died from starvation; Clearances of estates; Western counties worst hit; Emigrants supported Fenians, Land League & 1916 Rising; Cottiers & labourers worst hit; Irish at home & abroad blamed British government for the famine; The population fell by 2 million.

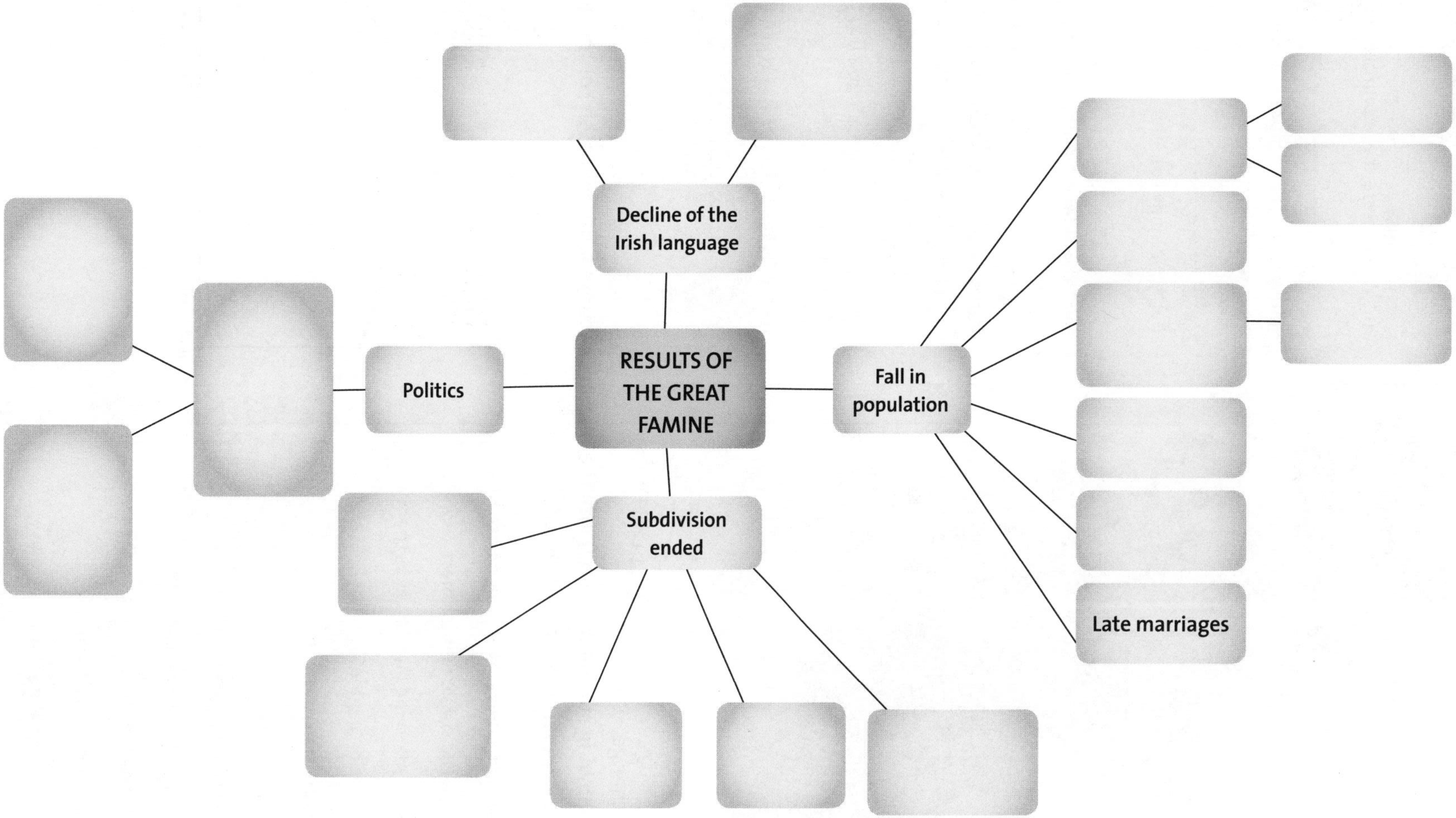

❼ Emigration, 1851–1911. ☆ Numeracy

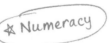

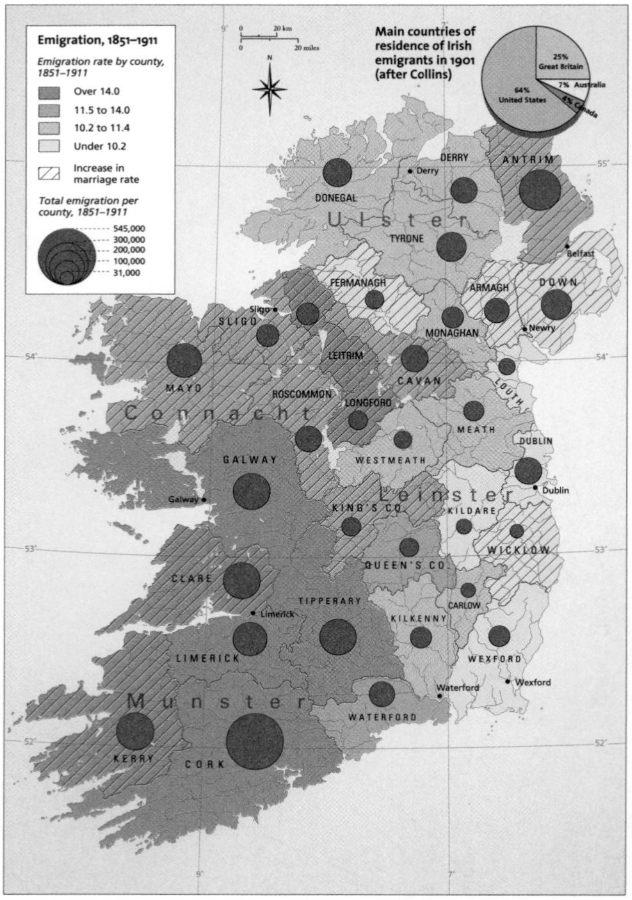

(i) How many counties had (a) over 14% and (b) between 11.5% and 14% emigration between 1851 and 1911?

(a) ____________ (b) ____________

(ii) Where were these counties located in Ireland?

____

(iii) Why did these counties have heavier emigration than the others?

____

(iv) How many counties had decreases in the marriage rate? ____________

(v) Why did the marriage rate decrease in these counties?

____

(vi) How does your county rate in relation to (a) emigration and (b) marriage rate?

(a) ____________ (b) ____________

(vii) What is the approximate total emigration from your county? ____________

(viii) Where did most of the Irish emigrate to?

____

❽ Population change, 1801–1911 ☆ Numeracy

Mark the following statements (1–12) into the relevant sections (approximately) of the graph of population change. One number is marked in already.

1.	High marriage rates and high birth rates
2.	Potato the staple diet for most people
3.	People marrying late, lower birth rate
4.	Emigration beginning
5.	Sub-division common
6.	Sub-division ending
7.	Heavy emigration continues
8.	Death from disease and starvation
9.	Population decline mainly due to emigration
10.	Blight destroys potato crops
11.	The Irish diaspora grows rapidly
12.	Irish language speakers decline in number

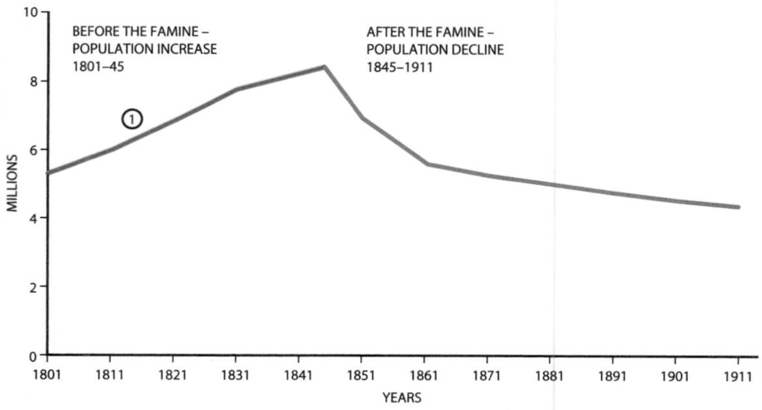

20 Towards an Independent Ireland, 1900–22

Key ideas

Political groups – Nationalists – self-government for Ireland; Home Rule Party largest, leader John Redmond; Home Rule better for Ireland, Parliament in Dublin for internal affairs, parliament in London for external affairs; King/Queen of both countries; IRB (Irish Republican Brotherhood), secret revolutionary organisation, complete independence, a republic, use of force; Sinn Féin, founder Arthur Griffith, dual monarchy, tariffs to protect industry, parliamentary abstentionism. **Unionists** – wanted to maintain rule from London, mostly in Ulster, leaders Carson and Craig, 'Home Rule is Rome Rule', markets for industry in Britain; Liberal Party supported Home Rule; Conservative Party supported unionists.

Cultural Nationalism: Irish – Ireland, Gaelic Ireland; Gaelic Athletic Association (GAA) (1884), Michael Cusack, Maurice Davin, promote hurling and football; Gaelic League (1893), Eoin MacNeill, Douglas Hyde, use of Irish language, de-Anglicise Ireland; Anglo-Irish literary movement, Irish literature in the English language, W.B. Yeats; influenced political thinking – full independence only through a Gaelic Ireland.

Labour Movement – Jim Larkin – founded ITGWU (Irish Transport and General Workers' Union), Dublin Strike and Lockout 1913, tramways, Employers' Federation, William Martin Murphy, James Connolly founded Irish Citizen Army.

Home Rule Crisis, 1912–1914 – Parliament Act 1911, House of Lords veto lifted, Third Home Rule Bill, 1912 – law by 1914. Unionist resistance – demonstrations, Ulster Solemn League and Covenant, Ulster Volunteer Force (UVF) 100,000, Larne gunrunning – arms from Germany; support from Conservative Party; Curragh Mutiny; nationalist reaction – Eoin MacNeill – 'The North Began'; Irish Volunteers founded, landed arms in Howth with Asgard; threat of civil war between nationalists and unionists; threat ended by World War I; Home Rule postponed until after the war.

Reaction to World War I – unionists supported the war effort; joined British army to protect the Union; nationalist split – Redmond supported war effort; majority follow him as National Volunteers; minority in Irish Volunteers against war, led by Eoin MacNeill; 250,000 Irishmen joined British army – Royal Munster Fusiliers, Irish Guards – to win Home Rule for Ireland, 30,000 to 50,000 killed in war.

1916 Rising – planned by IRB – 'England's difficulty is Ireland's opportunity', rising during the world war; Military Council led by Clarke, Pearse, McDermott – Casement to Germany for arms, sent in *Aud*; Easter Sunday set for Rising, Connolly brought in with Irish Citizen Army; MacNeill fooled by Castle Document (British plan to arrest Volunteer leaders), sanctions, Volunteer manoeuvres for Sunday; plans go wrong – *Aud* captured off Kerry, Casement arrested too, Castle Document a forgery – MacNeill cancelled manoeuvres; Rising set for Easter Monday – Dublin affair – 1,500 Volunteers and Irish Citizen Army; capture GPO, Proclamation read; Jacob's Factory, Boland's Mills, Four Courts; British army reinforcements from Curragh and England; *Helga* gunboat on Liffey shelling; Pearse surrendered on Saturday.

Results – 500 killed (including 300 civilians), 2,500 injured, £3 million damages, people angry with rebel leaders; martial law and internment of 3,000 (many innocent), 15 leaders executed; sympathy from people. Rise of Sinn Féin – de Valera President of Sinn Féin and Irish Volunteers; won by-elections, helped by conscription crisis and German plot; younger members won 1918 General Election – took over from Home Rule Party.

Independence Struggle, 1919–21 – Sinn Féin – passive resistance; First Dáil – Declaration of Independence; alternative government – de Valera as President of Dáil, Griffith Minister of Home Affairs, Collins Minister of Finance; control of county and city councils, Sinn Féin courts, Dáil loan; Irish Volunteers (later Irish Republican Army, IRA) – guerrilla warfare; first shots at Soloheadbeg, Co. Tipperary; attacks on RIC – hit and run, attacks on barracks for arms. Collins, Director of Intelligence, spies as porters, secretaries and police including Dublin Metropolitan Police; Squad to assassinate detectives, British spies; flying columns, e.g. Tom Barry, Seán MacEoin, ambushes – Kilmichael, Crossbarry, Co. Cork; Lloyd George, British Prime Minister, brought in ex-soldiers as Black and Tans, ex-officers as Auxiliaries – reprisals on people, helped IRA; Government of Ireland Act 1920 – two parliaments, Dublin and Belfast, rejected by Sinn Féin; RIC murder Tomás MacCurtain, Lord Mayor of Cork; Terence MacSwiney, also Lord Mayor, died after 74 days' hunger strike in Brixton Prison; Bloody Sunday, Squad kill British agents, Black and Tans kill 12 in Croke Park; IRA attack Custom House, Dublin, 80 Dublin IRA captures. Peace – IRA running out of ammunition, people want peace, British government criticised by harsh tactics; ceasefire agreed.

Anglo–Irish Treaty – negotiations in London; Irish delegation – Griffith, Collins, Barton, Duggan, Childers; wanted a republic, no partition between North and South; de Valera did not go – head of state, watch extremists at home; British delegation – Lloyd George, Churchill, Birkenhead, Chamberlain; wanted Ireland in the British Commonwealth; terms – Ireland known as Irish Free State, dominion of British Commonwealth, Governor-General to represent King in Ireland, oath of allegiance for Dáil and Senate, three Treaty ports – Berehaven, Cobh and Lough Swilly, Boundary Commission to decide border. Treaty debates – in Dáil; For, pro-Treaty – Griffith, Collins; IRA not strong enough, Treaty a stepping stone to independence, more independence than Home Rule; Against, anti-Treaty – de Valera, Brugha; did not get republic, better terms could be negotiated, against oath of allegiance, recognised king as head of state; majority in favour (64 to 57).

Irish Civil War – pro-Treaty, Regulars, government forces against anti-Treaty, Irregulars, Republican forces; both sides took over vacated British barracks; Republicans took over Four Courts; general election in favour of Treaty; Collins, commander-in-chief, attacked Four Courts, defeated Republicans in Dublin; Munster Republic – line from Limerick to Waterford – Republican territory; government forces captured Limerick and Waterford, sent ships to Cork, Fenit (Co. Kerry); Griffith died of haemorrhage, Collins killed in ambush at Béal na mBláth; Cosgrave and O'Higgins in charge; Republicans use guerrilla warfare but not supported by people; death of Liam Lynch, leader of anti-Treaty IRA; ceasefire; results – 900 killed, £30 million damages, bitterness between both sides, loss of ablest leaders – Griffith, Collins, origins of political parties, Cumann na nGaedheal (later Fine Gael) pro-Treaty; Sinn Féin (later Fianna Fáil) anti-Treaty.

1 Match each Key Term with the corresponding explanation. Literacy

1	Unionism	A	Complete independence from Britain
2	Home Rule	B	Favours government control of agriculture and industry
3	Nationalism	C	Maintain the union with Britain
4	Republicanism	D	All people divided into nations and nations should have self-government
5	Socialism	E	Self-government in Ireland with control of domestic affairs

1	
2	
3	
4	
5	

2 Explain the following Key Terms in relation to **Ireland in the early 20th century.** Literacy

Auxiliaries	
Black and Tans	
Bloody Sunday, 1920	
Dominion status	
Flying columns	
Partition	
Squad	
Ulster Solemn League and Covenant	

3. Fill in the missing words in relation to **the Home Rule Crisis** in the following sentences.

(i) John R____________ was leader of the Home Rule Party from 1900 to 1918.

(ii) The introduction of the 1911 P____________ Act meant that Home Rule would become law by 1914.

(iii) To resist Home Rule, Unionists set up the Ulster V____________ Force.

(iv) The Irish Volunteers smuggled arms into the country at H____________, Co. Dublin, on 26 July 1914.

(v) British army officers threatened to resign if they were ordered to enforce Home Rule in Ulster. This was known as the C ____________ Mutiny.

(vi) Civil war was prevented by the outbreak of the First W____________ ____________ in August 1914.

4. Match each name with the corresponding description. ☆ Literacy

1	Sir Edward Carson	A	Home Rule politician
2	Arthur Griffith	B	British political leader
3	John Redmond	C	Howth gun-running
4	Herbert Asquith	D	Leader during the 1913 Strike and Lockout
5	The Irish Volunteers	E	Sinn Féin leader
6	James Larkin	F	Unionist leader in Ireland

1	
2	
3	
4	
5	
6	

5. Identify each of the Irish political leaders (1–10) and link them with the relevant comments (A–J) You may need to research online for these.

Comments	
A	'Blood is a cleansing and sanctifying thing, and the nation that regards it as the final horror has lost its manhood.'
B	He wrote *The Resurrection of Hungary*.
C	'The cause of labour is the cause of Ireland, the cause of Ireland is the cause of labour.'
D	Fought in Stephen's Green during the 1916 Rising
E	Gave the countermanding order at Easter 1916
F	'In my opinion it gives us freedom, not the ultimate freedom that all nations desire, but the freedom to achieve it.'
G	'I am against this Treaty not because I am a man of war but because I am a man of peace.'
H	Leader of the Home Rule Party
I	'We must be prepared, the morning Home Rule passes, ourselves to become responsible for the government of the Protestant Province of Ulster.'
J	Union leader of the 1913 Strike and Lockout

Leader's name	Comment
1	
2	
3	
4	
5	
6	
7	
8	
9	
10	

❻ Chronology

Put the following events relating to the **1916 Rising** in chronological order, 1 (oldest)–10. ☆ Numeracy

Events		Dates	Order
1	Military Council decided the rising would go ahead on Easter Monday		
2	MacNeill found out the Castle Document was a forgery		
3	*Aud* captured off the Kerry coast		
4	Volunteer manoeuvres for Easter Sunday cancelled		
5	World War I began		
6	The Military Council sent Roger Casement to Germany to get arms and ammunition		
7	The IRB formed the Military Council		
8	Eoin MacNeill given Castle Document		
9	Roger Casement captured in Kerry		
10	The Military Council decided on a rising for Easter 1916		

❼ Fill in the missing words in relation to **the War of Independence** in the following sentences. ☆ Literacy

(i) The War of Independence began when the IRA attacked an RIC patrol at ____________, Co. Tipperary.

(ii) The IRA was organised into local units known as Flying ____________

(iii) The IRA used ____________ warfare or ambush tactics against the British forces.

(iv) The British government recruited ex-soldiers known as the ____________ and ____________ to support the RIC.

(v) Michael Collins, Director of Intelligence, set up a ____________ of twelve assassins to kill British spies.

(vi) The Government of ____________ Act was passed in 1920 but the fighting continued until the truce in July 1921.

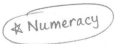

8 Put the following events relating to the **War of Independence** in chronological order, 1 (earliest)–9. ✯ Numeracy

Events		Dates	Order
1	Tomás MacCurtain murdered		
2	Kilmichael Ambush		
3	Sinn Féin won 73 seats in the general election		
4	Bloody Sunday		
5	Ceasefire		
6	Terence McSwiney died on hunger strike		
7	IRA attack on the Custom House, Dublin		
8	The burning of Cork City centre		
9	The meeting of the first Dáil Éireann		

9 Fill in the missing words in relation to **the Anglo-Irish Treaty** in the following sentences. ✯ Literacy

(i) De Valera went to London in July 1921, but failed to reach agreement with Prime Minister, L__________ G__________ on the terms of a treaty.

(ii) In October 1921 an Irish delegation led by G__________ and Collins took part in Treaty talks with the British government.

(iii) The Irish delegates were treaty plenipotentiaries, but De Valera ordered them to consult him before s__________ any treaty.

(iv) The British Prime Minister put pressure on the Irish delegates to sign an agreement. He threatened immediate and terrible w__________.

(v) On 6 December 1921 the A__________ I__________ Treaty, which ended the War of Independence, was signed by the delegates.

(vi) Ireland would be known as the I__________ F__________ S__________

(vii) Ireland would be a d__________ of the B__________ C__________

(viii) Britain would have the use of t__________ T__________ ports.

(ix) A B__________ C__________ would be set up to decide on the border between the north and south of Ireland.

(x) The Treaty divided the Dáil and the IRA. It led to a C__________ War.

10 Which of the following were **pro-Treaty arguments** and which were **anti-Treaty arguments**? Tick under each heading as appropriate.

	Pro-Treaty	Anti-Treaty
The oath of allegiance recognised the king as head of state		
The IRA was not able to carry on a war any longer.		
The Treaty was a stepping stone to full independence.		
The Treaty did not give Ireland the republic that they had fought for.		
The Treaty gave Ireland much more independence than Home Rule.		
Better terms could have been negotiated.		

11 Fill in the missing words below in relation to the **Irish Civil War** in the following sentences. ✩ Literacy

The Civil War was caused by divisions over the A____________-I____________ T____________.

The two sides were known as the R____________ and the I____________

The Anti-Treaty forces captured a F____________ S____________ general.

The Government forces began the shelling of the F____________ C____________ in D____________.

The Anti-Treaty forces retreated behind a line from L____________ to W____________.

A____________ G____________ died from a brain haemmorhage.

M____________ C____________ was killed in an ambush at B____________ na mB____________ in Co. C____________.

The Civil War resulted in the destruction of D____________ for the second time in s____________ years.

The Civil War resulted in the deaths of many fine I____________.

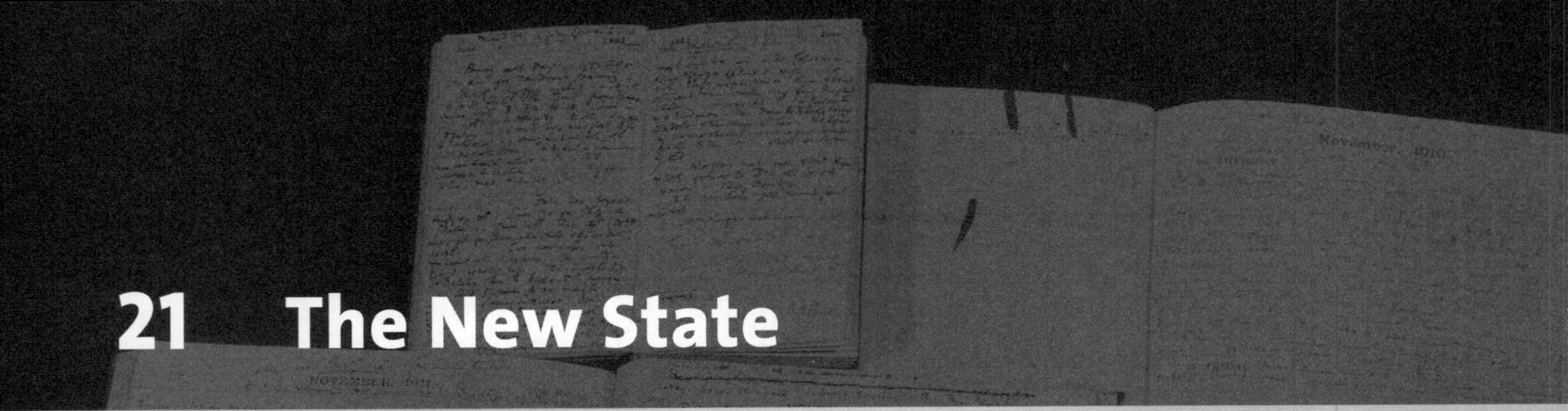

21 The New State

Key ideas

The New State, Cumann na nGaedheal in power, 1922–32 – Cosgrave President of Executive Council; establish law and order, pass Constitution – Irish Free State, member of British Commonwealth, oath of allegiance for Dáil and Senate, king's representative = Governor-General; set up Garda Síochána, new courts, Public Safety Act – powers of arrest; Army Mutiny – reduced size of army, slow progress to republic, officers object, Kevin O'Higgins arrested leaders, Minister for Defence, Mulcahy, had to resign; democracy strengthened. **Economy** – agriculture most important industry, better standards for eggs, dairy, improved breeding methods, loans for farmers, lower taxes, agriculture exports to Britain increased; Shannon Scheme – £5 million dam at Ardnacrusha, on Shannon, ESB set up, electricity for industry. **Relations with Britain** – Boundary Commission to adjust border with North, Eoin MacNeill Free State representative, few changes to border but took some land from South to North, Cumann na nGaedheal government disappointed; Irish Free State worked with Australia, Canada to get more independence from Britain, Statute of Westminster – power to change laws made by British government. **Decline of Cumann na nGaedheal** – failure of Boundary Commission, Great Depression, rising unemployment, cut pay of teachers, gardaí, cut old age pension, Fianna Fáil founded – de Valera left Sinn Féin because of abstentionist policy; Fianna Fáil won 1932 general election.

Fianna Fáil in power, 1932–39 – peaceful transfer of power to de Valera. **Dismantling the Treaty** – de Valera used the Statute of Westminster to dismantle Treaty – abolished oath, office of Governor-General, removed king as head of state, wrote new Constitution – new name, Ireland or Éire, Articles 2 and 3 claimed right to rule Northern Ireland, President head of state – Douglas Hyde, Taoiseach head of government, 'special position' of Catholic Church. **IRA and Blueshirts** – de Valera released IRA prisoners, they attacked Cumann na nGaedheal meetings, ACA (Army Comrades Association) – ex-soldiers of Free State army – protected Cumann na nGaedheal meetings, Eoin O'Duffy leader, planned march in Dublin to commemorate Griffith and Collins, banned by de Valera, Blueshirts joined with Cumann na nGaedheal to form Fine Gael, O'Duffy leader but bad leader, dropped, went to Spain to help Franco in Spanish Civil War.

Economic War – de Valera refused to pay land annuities to Britain, Britain imposed taxes on Irish imports, Ireland put taxes on British imports, unemployment rose, cattle exports hit; ended by Anglo-Irish Agreement – de Valera paid lump sum £10 million for land annuities, taxes on imports dropped, Treaty ports given to Irish government; Seán Lemass, Minister of Industry and Commerce, put taxes on imports to protect Irish industry (protectionism), also set up Irish Sugar Company and Aer Lingus.

The Emergency (Ireland during World War II) – Ireland neutral – why? showed independence, Northern Ireland part of UK, Ireland too weak to fight stronger powers; Emergency Powers Act gave government great power to control country; built up defence forces, censored news reports on radio and papers; helped Allies – allowed British planes to fly over Donegal, released British and American airmen. Dangers to neutrality: IRA – wanted German help to invade Northern Ireland, de Valera crushed IRA, execution, death on hunger strike. Germany – spies to Ireland, arrested, IRA too weak, 'Operation Green' – plan to invade Ireland, bombed South – North Strand, Dublin, 34 killed. Britain – wanted Ireland to join war, Churchill, Prime Minister, offered to end partition after the war; de Valera rejected it; Britain used North for sea patrols and to prepare for D-Day. America – said South would be used by Germans to spy on D-Day preparations. Shortages, rationing – Lemass, Minister for Supplies, brought chartered ships to bring supplies, rationing of food, clothes, petrol, ration books and coupons, black market for supplies; glimmer men (gas inspectors) to check houses, turf instead of coal, factories laid off workers, emigration to Britain.

First Inter-Party government, 1948–51 – defeat for de Valera in 1948 general election – people wanted change, unemployment, emigration and shortages continued; new government a coalition government of Fine Gael, Labour, Clann na Poblachta; Taoiseach John A. Costello, Seán McBride Minister for Foreign Affairs, Noel Browne Minister for Health; declared Ireland a republic, set up IDA (Industrial Development Authority) to attract industry, got Marshall Aid for houses and hospitals, rural electrification, Browne successful in public health – TB campaign; Mother and Child Scheme (free medicine for children under 16 and mothers) caused conflict, opposed by Catholic Church and doctors; rest of the 1950s – high unemployment and emigration, changes of government between Fianna Fáil and Second Inter-Party Government; de Valera resigned, elected President, Seán Lemass became Taoiseach.

Seán Lemass and 1960s – appointed young ministers – Jack Lynch, Charles Haughey. Economy – new economic policy, First Programme for Economic Expansion; ended protectionism (tariffs); encouraged exports, tax concessions and grants to attract foreign industry (British, American); successful – unemployment, emigration down, people better off, population rose.

Northern Ireland – Lemass's view – end partition (unite country) by making South more prosperous; met Terence O'Neill, Northern PM, in Belfast, O'Neill came to Dublin. Education – Donagh O'Malley, Minister for Education, new schools, improved old ones, new courses, brought in free secondary education, student numbers increased. Social change: shopping centres built, more tourists, RTÉ set up – new ideas, 'Swinging Sixties', Ireland active in **United Nations**, President Kennedy came to Ireland.

Jack Lynch as Taoiseach – Lynch succeeded Lemass. **Northern Ireland** – the Troubles – some ministers wanted to send the Irish army to Derry or to give arms to nationalists, Lynch dismissed Charles Haughey and Neil Blaney; charged in relation to the illegal importation of arms; Blaney charges dropped, Haughey acquitted. **EEC** – Lynch negotiated terms of Ireland's entry to European Economic Community, people in favour because of economic benefits, people opposed due to loss of independence – huge majority in favour in referendum.

Coalition government – Fine Gael–Labour Party government, Liam Cosgrave as Taoiseach; Ireland joined EEC on 1 January, 1973 (along with Britain and Denmark). Effects – Ireland benefited, Common Agricultural Policy – higher prices for farmers and grants, American companies attracted to Ireland because of huge EEC market, small industries closed due to competition, grants for job training, roads, sewerage, telephones. Oil crisis – oil prices rise, caused unemployment, inflation; government increased taxes and borrowings, unpopular. Northern Ireland, the Troubles – Cosgrave signed Sunningdale Agreement with Ted Heath, British Prime Minister – power-sharing government in NI, Council of Ireland giving South greater say in North, loyalist (extreme unionist) bombings in Dublin and Monaghan, 33 killed.

Jack Lynch as Taoiseach – popular election manifesto – grants for first-time house buyers, abolition of some taxes; Charles Haughey back as minister – Lynch lost some by-elections, Lynch resigned, Haughey elected as Taoiseach.

Political developments in 1980s – instability in government – high unemployment and inflation – governments alternate between coalition governments and Fianna Fáil; Garret FitzGerald, Taoiseach of coalition government. Northern Ireland – New Ireland Forum – political parties North and South shared ideas for solving Northern Ireland's problems. Anglo-Irish Agreement – between FitzGerald and Margaret Thatcher, British Prime Minister, South had greater say in Northern Ireland – led to closer links between Irish government and British government in solving Northern Ireland's problems.

1 Match each Key Term with the corresponding explanation. Literacy

1	Boundary Commission	A	Border separating Northern Ireland from Éire or Republic of Ireland
2	Democracy	B	Three-member group who investigated border between northern and southern Ireland
3	Shannon Scheme	C	Power to Commonwealth countries, including Ireland, to change any laws passed by the British government for that country
4	Statute of Westminster	D	Political power comes from the people who vote for leaders in a general election
5	Partition	E	Government plan in the 1920s to build hydroelectric scheme on the Shannon

1	
2	
3	
4	
5	

2 Explain each of the following terms in relation to **Cumann na nGaedheal in government.** ✩ Literacy

Army Mutiny

____

____

Law and order

____

____

Dominion status

____

____

Balfour Declaration

____

____

Great Depression

____

____

3 Put these events in relation to Ireland in the 1920s and 1930s in chronological order by writing in the dates. When you have the dates (1–8), mark the events (1–8) above the appropriate point on the timeline below. ✩ Numeracy

Events		Dates	Order
1	New Constitution, Bunreacht na hÉireann, passed		
2	Boundary Commission report		
3	Shannon Scheme finished		
4	Army Mutiny		
5	Fianna Fáil in power for the first time		
6	De Valera abolished the Oath of Allegiance		
7	Founding of the Garda Síochána		
8	Anglo-Irish Agreement		

1920 ———————————————————————— 1934

4 Which of the following were **achievements of Cumann na nGaedheal in government, 1923–1932?** Tick the appropriate box.

Historical skills

Events	Achievements
The founding of the Garda Síochána	
The re-organisation of the courts system	
The establishment of law and order	
The quelling of the Army Mutiny	
The building of the Shannon Scheme	
Fighting the Economic War	
The Boundary Commission report	
The passing of the Statue of Westminster	
Improving standards in agriculture	
Increasing agricultural exports to Britain	
The abolition of the Oath of Allegiance	
Setting up the ESB (Electricity Supply Board)	
Dealing with the effects of the Great Depression in Ireland	

5 Match each person with the corresponding event/organisation.

1	Douglas Hyde	A	New Constitution
2	William T. Cosgrave	B	Founder of Sinn Féin
3	Éamon de Valera	C	Minister for Home Affairs
4	Arthur Griffith	D	The Blueshirts
5	Kevin O'Higgins	E	President of Ireland
6	Eoin O'Duffy	F	Cumann na nGaedheal

1	
2	
3	
4	
5	
6	

Literacy

Historical skills

❻ Match up the beginning and end of these sentences on **Fianna Fáil in Power**.

1	De Valera was able to use the terms of the Statute of Westminster	A	from the Irish Free State to Ireland (or Éire).
2	The British government raised protests about these changes to the Anglo-Irish Treaty	B	the 'special position' of the Catholic Church.
3	In the new Constitution, the name of the country was changed	C	composed of ex-soldiers of the Free State army.
4	Articles 2 and 3 of the Constitution	D	but could do nothing about them.
5	The state recognised	E	whose members thought de Valera was not doing enough to establish a republic.
6	When de Valera took over the government	F	to dismantle (take apart) the Anglo-Irish Treaty.
7	An Army Comrades Association (ACA) was	G	with the Anglo-Irish Agreement of 1938.
8	De Valera was faced with problems from the IRA	H	de Valera stopped paying land annuities to Britain.
9	Soon after taking over the government,	I	to build up Irish industry.
10	The 'economic war' came to an end	J	he released IRA prisoners.
11	Fianna Fáil believed in using protectionism	K	claimed the right to rule over Northern Ireland.

1	
2	
3	
4	
5	
6	
7	
8	
9	
10	
11	

❼ Fill in the blank spaces in this account of the **Emergency in Ireland** from the word list below. (Some words may be used more than once)

Word List: Emergency; newspaper; Donegal; hunger strike; neutral; rationing; defence; Churchill; Allies; independence; partition; emigrated; USA; France; Germany; D-Day; soldiers; de Valera; market; censored; ration; Allied; fertilisers; IRA.

Ireland stayed ____________ during World War II because it showed Ireland's ____________ from Britain. The government, led by ____________, passed the ____________ Powers Act, which gave it great power to control the country. Ireland built up its ____________ forces, increasing them from about 20,000 to almost 250,000 part-time and full-time ____________. The government also ____________ radio and ____________ reports. Even though it was ____________, the Irish government favoured the ____________ (Britain, ____________ and the United States). For example, ____________ planes were allowed fly over ____________ from Northern Ireland. The country faced danger to its neutrality from the IRA, ____________ and even Britain and the USA. The ____________ wanted to get help from Germany so that they could invade Northern Ireland. But de Valera arrested and imprisoned ____________ leaders; some were executed, and some died on ____________ ____________.

Britain wanted Ireland to join the war and ____________, the British Prime Minister, said ____________ would end if Ireland joined the war. But de Valera rejected this offer. The ____________ thought Ireland would be used as a base for German spies who would spy on American preparations for ____________ in Northern Ireland. Ireland had to introduce ____________ due to shortages of imports so people were given ____________ books for food, clothes and footwear. But people were able to use the 'black ____________' to get some of these goods. Industry and agriculture were hit by the shortages such as coal and ____________. Workers were laid off and some ____________ to Britain to work in war industries there or join the British army.

8 Match the terms in Column A with the explanations in Column B. ☆ Literacy

Column A		Column B	
1	Inter-Party government	A	Bringing up to date
2	Coalition government	B	The level of necessities, comforts and wealth available to an individual or a group
3	Rural electrification	C	Name given to first coalition government
4	Modernisation	D	Public health scheme
5	Mother and Child Scheme	E	Government formed by a number of political parties
6	Standard of living	F	Bringing electricity to the countryside

1	
2	
3	
4	
5	
6	

9 Explain the following terms from **Ireland in the 20th century.** ☆ Literacy

The Arms Crisis	
Referendum	
The 'Troubles'	
Sunningdale Agreement	
New Ireland Forum	
Anglo-Irish Agreement, 1985	

10 Circle the **five incorrect words/phrases** in the passage below and insert the correct words in the box on the side.

Literacy

During World War II, Germany sent troops to Ireland. The Germans hoped to join forces with the UVF. But they soon found that the UVF was too weak. The troops themselves were quickly arrested. The Germans had a plan to invade Ireland – 'Operation Orange'. But they considered the air journey to Ireland too long and too dangerous. However, the south of Ireland was bombed on a number of occasions by German planes. The most serious bombing was in the Phoenix Park in Dublin in May 1941, when thirty-four people were killed.

1	
2	
3	
4	
5	

11 Which of the following statements about **the First Inter-Party Government, 1948–51** are true, and which are false? Please tick the appropriate box.

	True	False
De Valera and Fianna Fáil lost the 1948 general election because people wanted a change.		
The First Inter-Party Government was a coalition government made up of three main parties: Fine Gael, Labour and Clann na Talmhan.		
The Taoiseach was Seán MacBride.		
John A. Costello was the Minister for External Affairs.		
In 1949, the government declared Ireland a republic but Ireland remained in the British Commonwealth.		
The government set up the Industrial Development Authority (IDA) to attract foreign industry.		
Ireland got Marshall Aid money from America.		
A scheme of rural electrification provided houses in the countryside with electricity.		
Dr Noel Browne, Minister for Health, organised a campaign against TB (tuberculosis).		
Dr Browne proposed a Mother and Child Scheme to give free medical help to mothers, and to children under sixteen.		
He was supported by the Catholic Church and by doctors.		

❶❷ Population change, 1926–61

★ Numeracy

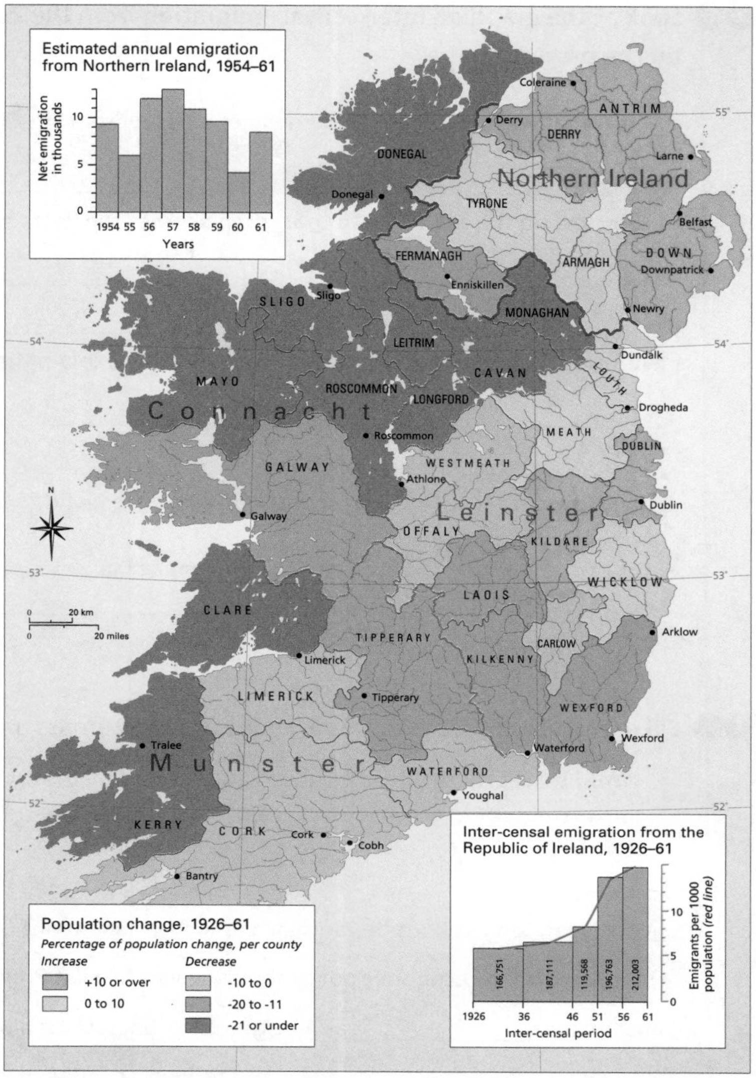

(i) Name the counties in Éire/the Republic of Ireland which had an increase of 10% or more.

___

(ii) Suggest two reasons why these counties experienced an increase.

___

___

(iii) How many counties had a 21% or more decrease? ___

(iv) Suggest two reasons why these counties experienced a decrease.

___

___

(v) Overall, how does population change in Northern Ireland compare with the South of Ireland?

___

___

13 Look at the graph on Inter-censal emigration from the Republic of Ireland, 1926–61 on the previous page.

☆ Numeracy

(i) What was the total number who emigrated from Éire/Republic of Ireland between 1926 and 1961?

____

(ii) How do the years 1951 to 1961 compare with the years before that? Explain the difference.

____

____

(iii) How does the information in the graph help explain the changes in the map on population change, 1926–61?

____

____

(iv) How did the Irish governments of the time respond to the population and emigration changes?

____

____

14 Fill in the blank spaces in this account of **Seán Lemass and the 1960s** from the word list below.

Word List: Partition; fifties; Fianna Fáil; emigration; tourists; free; modernising; better off; Economic Expansion; prosperous; RTÉ; 1961; shopping; twice; exports; Swinging Sixties; grants; Catholic; quickly; O'Neill; O'Malley; Lynch; new.

When Seán Lemass became Taoiseach in 1959, he set about the job of ____________ the country. Lemass introduced a new economic policy. It was called the First Programme for ____________ ____________. He encouraged ____________ and he gave tax concessions and ____________ to attract foreign industry. Employment rose and ____________ stopped. Living standards also rose, so people were ____________ ____________. The population began to increase from ____________ onwards. In relation to Northern Ireland, he believed that the best way to end ____________ was to make southern Ireland more ____________. He met Terence ____________, Prime Minister of Northern Ireland, ____________, once in Belfast and once in Dublin. Under Lemass, school courses were changed, ____________ schools were built and older ones were improved. The Minister for Education, Donagh ____________, brought in a scheme of ____________ secondary education. Numbers going to secondary schools increased ____________. People were better off in Ireland in the 1960s. There were many changes in the way people lived. The first ____________ centres were built. More ____________ came to the country. The ____________ Church brought in many reforms. ____________ was set up and television brought new ideas to the country. These were the '____________ ____________', in contrast to the depressed ____________. When Seán Lemass retired in 1966, he was succeeded by Jack ____________ as Taoiseach and as leader of ____________ ____________. Lemass had accomplished a great deal in a short time.

15 Identify each of the Irish political leaders (1–7) and link them with the relevant comments (A–G).

1

2

3

4

5

6

7

Comments	
A	He was a controversial Taoiseach.
B	'The country is, I think, like an aeroplane at the take-off stage.'
C	Taoiseach of the First Inter-Party government, 1948-51
D	He signed the Anglo-Irish Agreement, 1985
E	He captained the Cork hurling team.
F	He was the son of the first President of the Executive Council in the Irish Free State.
G	'From the moment this war began, there was, for this state, only one policy possible, neutrality.'

Leader's name	Comment
1	
2	
3	
4	
5	
6	
7	

16 Which of the following statements about **Political Developments in the 1970s** are true, and which are false? Tick the appropriate boxes.

	True	False
Taoiseach Jack Lynch had no difficulties even though violence increased in Northern Ireland.		
Some unionists in the South wanted to take an active part in the Northern Ireland conflict.		
In 1969, Jack Lynch made a television broadcast after the Battle of Derry.		
In 1970, Lynch faced a crisis arising out of the conflict in Northern Ireland when he had to dismiss two of his ministers – Seán Lemass and Neil Blaney.		
Lemass and Blaney were charged in relation to the illegal importation of arms.		
Lynch's government was also involved in negotiating Ireland's entry into the European Free Trade Association (EFTA).		
Some believed that Ireland's economy would benefit from membership of the EFTA.		
A referendum (a vote of the people) in 1972 resulted in a huge majority in favour of entering the EEC.		
Ireland benefited from membership of the EEC as guaranteed prices and grants under the Common Agricultural Policy (CAP) made farmers better off.		
Foreign companies, especially American ones, were attracted to Ireland, seeing it as a base from which to sell their products to the large EEC market.		
Ireland benefited from aid (grants) to provide job training and to improve roads, sewerage and telephone services.		
Jack Lynch and Fianna Fáil won the 1973 general election.		
A coalition government led by Liam Cosgrave was formed by Fine Gael and Labour.		
In the 1970s the economy ran into trouble as oil prices increased.		
Ireland suffered as unemployment rose and inflation fell.		
The Taoiseach, Liam Cosgrave, signed the Sunningdale Agreement in 1973 with the British Prime Minister, Brian Faulkner.		
Unionist extremists destroyed both the power-sharing government in Belfast and the Council of Ireland.		
The Northern violence hit the South in 1974 when loyalist bombs in Dublin and Monaghan killed thirty-three people.		
In 1977, Jack Lynch and Fianna Fáil defeated the coalition government in the general election.		
Lynch's success was his undoing. He brought back into cabinet (government) Charles Haughey, whom he had sacked in 1970.		

17 Fill in the blank spaces in these statements about **Political Developments in the 1980s.**

1. Charles H______________ was defeated in the 1981 general election.
2. A new coalition government of Fine Gael and L______________, led by Garret F______________.
3. The coalition was followed by another H______________ government, which lasted only about ten months.
4. A second coalition government, also led by Garret F______________, now took over.
5. The New I______________ F______________ was organised in Dublin where leaders from N______________ and S______________ shared their ideas about solving the problems of Northern Ireland.
6. Garret F______________ and the Prime Minister of Britain, Margaret T______________, signed the A______________ -I______________ Agreement in 1985.

Revising Modern Ireland

★ Literacy

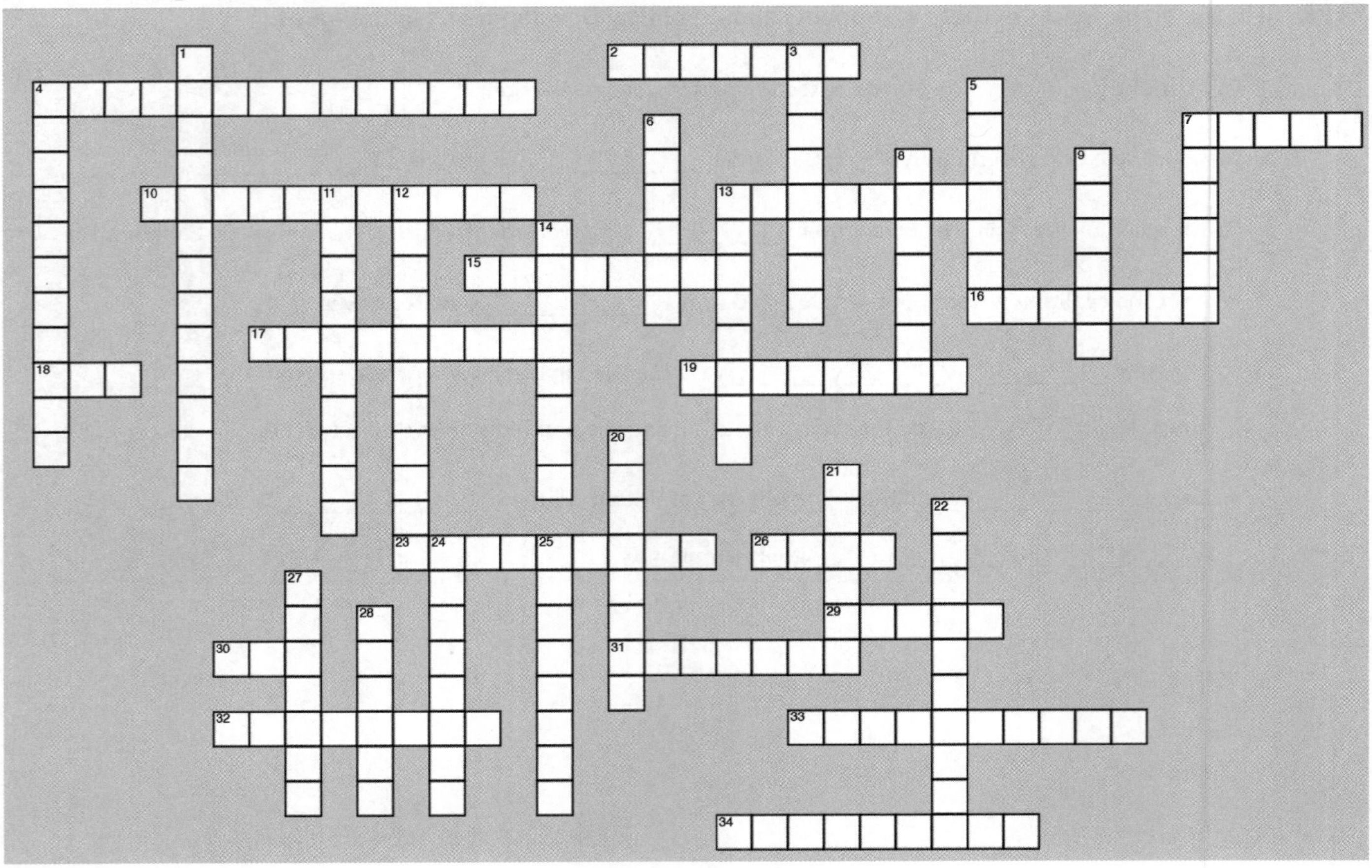

ACROSS

2 A battle between local people and RUC in Derry.
4 Unionists use power to worsen conditions for nationalist in Northern Ireland.
7 Signed the agreement that led Ireland into the EEC.
10 Statute that gave Ireland power to dismantle the Treaty.
13 Nationalism based on GAA and Gaelic League.
15 Conflict in Northern Ireland from 1969 onwards.
16 Hydroelectricity scheme in 1920s.
17 Division between North and South.
18 Short for Irish Republican Brotherhood.
19 Went to Germany to organise arms for Rising.
23 The name given to the period of World War II in Ireland.
26 Northern Ireland civil rights and nationalist leader.
29 Number of signatories of 1916 Proclamation.
30 German ship carrying arms to Ireland.
31 Limited food and clothes during World War II.
32 War between Britain and Ireland in 1930s.
33 Ambush led by Tom Barry in War of Independence.
34 Held power in Northern Ireland for most of 20th century.

DOWN

1 Policy of putting tariffs on imports.
3 Founder of Fianna Fail.
4 De Valera's changes to the Anglo-Irish Treaty.
5 Director of Intelligence during the War of Independence.
6 Forged document to convince Eoin MacNeill to order Volunteer activity before the 1916 Rising.
7 Leader of workers in 1913 Lockout.
8 Where Terence MacSwiney fasted to death.
9 Minister of Health, Mother and Child Scheme.
11 Another name for a coalition government.
12 Agreement to give the South a greater say in Northern Ireland.
13 Led Irish Free State in 1920s.
14 Founded Irish Citizen Army.
20 Commission set up to examine the border between North and South.
21 Taoiseach in 1960s.
22 Led by Eoin O'Duffy in 1930s.
24 Leader of the Irish Volunteers.
25 Founder of Sinn Fein.
27 Leader of the Home Rule Party.
28 Sunday in 1920, deaths of British secret service agents and Michael Hogan and supporters in Croke Park.

22 Northern Ireland: From Foundation to Attempts at Peace, 1920–85

Key ideas

Foundation – Government of Ireland Act 1920 set up parliament in Northern Ireland (based in Stormont after 1932) – in charge of internal affairs (roads, education); Westminster parliament in charge of external affairs (peace, war); Unionist Party in control, backed up by Orange Order (parades, marches); British government allowed unionists to run affairs, Craig Prime Minister until 1940.

Conflict with Catholics – Catholics wanted a united Ireland, Protestants opposed because of fear of discrimination; RUC, B-Specials used Special Powers Act to arrest anyone; Catholics suffered more in riots – more killed, lost jobs, e.g. Harland and Wolff, houses and businesses burned.

Discrimination – gerrymandering – constituency boundaries rigged to ensure unionist majority, e.g. Derry; Catholic schools got less help from government; Nationalist Party represented Catholics, took seats in parliament. Economy – decline in shipbuilding and linen, Great Depression, high unemployment – 40% in 1930s, poverty, hunger, children dying, pneumonia and TB. **Sectarian riots** – 1930s between Catholics and Protestants, Unionist politicians encouraged Protestants not to employ Catholics.

Northern Ireland in World War II – crucial role in war – planes and boats from NI patrolled North Atlantic for U-boats, 120,000 US troops used NI to prepare for D-Day; ships, aircraft, parachutes made for war; Churchill offered to end partition after war if South joined war effort; Craig objected, de Valera rejected Churchill's offer; Craig died, replaced by Andrews – inefficient, replaced by Basil Brooke (later Lord Brookeborough). Belfast bombed – poorly defended – seven anti-aircraft guns, no searchlights, heavily bombed by German bombers four times in April/May 1941, 900 killed, 450 injured in first attack, 200 killed in second attack, fire brigades from South came to help; but North and South drifted further apart during the war.

Post-war years after 1945 – Welfare State – thousands of houses built, Education Act 1947 – free secondary education, free medical care for mothers and children, TB campaign. **Partition** – anti-partition campaign begun by Northern nationalists, opposed by unionists – 'Ulster is not for sale'; South declared a republic in 1949 – Britain passed Ireland Act to guarantee Northern Ireland part of UK so long as Northern parliament wanted it; **IRA border campaign** – attacks on barracks, Brookeborough took action, also de Valera in the South, so IRA campaign ended.

Economy – decline of shipbuilding in 1960s due to German and Japanese competition, decline in linen due to competition from other textiles.

O'Neill, Civil Rights and the Troubles – O'Neill succeeded Brookeborough; attracted industry to NI, mostly around Belfast; improved relations with Catholics – met Cardinal Conway, Archbishop of Armagh, visited Catholic schools; relations with South – Taoiseach Lemass visited O'Neill in Belfast, O'Neill visited Dublin. Catholics and Protestants – some Protestants did not want O'Neill to improve relations with Catholics, e.g. Ian Paisley; Ulster Volunteer Force founded – Catholics killed; discrimination against Catholics – allocation of houses and jobs by local councils favoured Protestants; Civil Rights Association founded – aims: 'one man, one vote', end gerrymandering, end discrimination in jobs and housing; led by John Hume, Gerry Fitt, Austin Currie, Bernadette Devlin; civil rights march in Derry – clash with RUC, shown on television; O'Neill brought in reforms – opposed by Paisley – O'Neill forced to resign, succeeded as Prime Minister by James Chichester-Clark.

The Troubles – violence after Apprentice Boys march in Derry (1969) – nationalists barricaded Bogside, RUC tried to get in – Battle of the Bogside; British troops into Bogside and Belfast to protect Catholics/nationalists, welcomed; Social Democratic and Labour Party (SDLP) formed, led by Gerry Fitt and John Hume.

IRA – split between Official IRA and Provisional IRA – Provisional IRA (Provos) set up with encouragement of ministers of southern government, government money used to buy arms for Provos. **Internment** – Brian Faulkner Prime Minister – brought in internment (arrest and imprisonment without trial) – 342 arrested – many innocent people arrested, main IRA leaders escaped, widespread rioting afterwards, increased support for IRA. **Bloody Sunday** – British soldiers fired on anti-internment march in Derry – 13 people killed – widespread rioting afterwards; British embassy in Dublin burned. **Direct rule** from Westminster – British government suppressed Stormont parliament and government – North directly ruled from Westminster, William Whitelaw Secretary of State for Northern Ireland; attempts at peace: **Sunningdale Agreement** – Edward Heath, British Prime Minister, Liam Cosgrave, Taoiseach, agree on power-sharing government for NI, Council of Ireland to give South a say in running NI; Unionist Party, SDLP, Alliance Party share power; opposed by extreme unionists, e.g. Paisley; Ulster Workers' Council Strike – general strike in May 1974 – electricity supplies cut, roads blocked, power-sharing government ended – direct rule continued.

Hunger strikes – IRA prisoners in H-Blocks demanded political prisoner status, British Prime Minister Margaret Thatcher refused to give in; some prisoners went on hunger strike, death of Bobby Sands and nine others – caused greater divisions between unionists and nationalists in North.

Anglo-Irish Agreement (1985) – between Margaret Thatcher and Garret FitzGerald, Taoiseach – gave southern government say in running NI – formed basis for future progress in peace; other peace moves – Downing Street Declaration and Good Friday Agreement.

1 Fill in the information in the blank spaces in relation to **Northern Ireland.**

(i) Sir James ____________ was the first Prime Minister of Northern Ireland.

(ii) The ____________ party was the largest party in Northern Ireland in the 1920s.

(iii) ____________ was the practice of dividing up electoral districts in order to give some political party an advantage.

(iv) The Prime Minister of Northern Ireland from 1963 until 1969 was Sir Terence ____________

(v) The Civil Rights Movement was set up to campaign for better conditions for the ____________ minority.

(vi) ____________ or imprisonment without trial was introduced by the Northern Ireland government in 1971.

2 Fill in the blank spaces in the account of **Life in Northern Ireland during World War II.**

The German occupation of F____________ and the n____________ of southern Ireland meant that Northern Ireland played a crucial role in the war. Planes and boats based in Northern Ireland were used to p____________ the N____________ A____________. They had to look for German U-____________ and to protect c____________. When the U____________ S____________ entered the war in December 1941, Northern Ireland became an important b____________ for American troops. Some were manning ships to protect the A____________ trade, while others were preparing for D____________. W____________ and merchant ships by H____________ and W____________, over 1,600 aircraft from S____________, 500 tanks, p____________, rope and shells were all produced for the war effort. Un____________ fell to 5% from a pre-war level of 25%. The North's agriculture benefited from g____________ prices for its food on the British market; compulsory t____________ orders increased the acreage under f____________, oats and potatoes. C____________ was not enforced in Northern Ireland because of n____________ objections. R____________ of food, clothes and petrol was put in place. C____________, Prime Minister, offered de Valera the r____________ of Ireland after the war if southern Ireland joined the war. The Prime Minister, James C____________ objected strongly. De Valera rejected C____________ offer.

The ministers of the U______________ government were old and incompetent. C______________ was replaced as Prime Minister by J. M. A______________. He was replaced by Basil B______________. Belfast was an easy target for G______________ bombers but the U______________ government thought the city was too far away to be attacked. The city and its industries were heavily attacked f______________ times in April and May 1941. Over 1 ______________ people were killed in these attacks. Most of the people were killed in the most serious raid at E______________, when 180 G______________ b______________ attacked the city. In another attack serious damage was done to H______________ and W______________. Fire b______________ came from the s______________ of Ireland to help stop the fires. Thousands of people left the city each night to shelter in the surrounding c______________ until morning; some came to the s______________. H______________ the houses of the city were destroyed.

3 Put the following events in chronological order. Mark the events (1–12) above the appropriate point on the timeline below. ☆ Numeracy

Events		Dates	Order
1	Bloody Sunday		
2	SDLP founded		
3	O'Neill resigned		
4	The Ireland Act		
5	O'Neill becomes Prime Minister		
6	Seán Lemass goes to Stormont		
7	The Education Act		
8	NICRA founded		
9	Civil Rights march in Derry		
10	Internment introduced		
11	Apprentice Boys march in Derry/clashes in Bogside		
12	Direct Rule from Westminster brought in		

1945 ———————————————————————— 1973

4 Which of the following statements in relation to **Political Developments in Northern Ireland in the 1960s** are true, and which are false? Tick the appropriate boxes.

	True	False
Terence O'Neill succeeded Craig as Prime Minister.		
The O'Neill government attracted new industries to the mainly Protestant, western part of Ulster.		
O'Neill met the Catholic Cardinal Conway, Archbishop of Armagh.		
O'Neill refused to visit Catholic schools.		
O'Neill invited Taoiseach, Jack Lynch, to Stormont in 1965.		
O'Neill returned the visit by travelling to Dundalk.		
Extreme unionists were worried about O'Neill's efforts to improve relations with Catholics.		
The Ulster Volunteer Army (UVA) was formed.		
Catholics were disappointed that O'Neill was not bringing in more reforms.		
Catholics were still discriminated against in several areas.		
The property qualifications for voting in local elections favoured Protestants.		
The gerrymandering of constituencies meant nationalists controlled councils in unionist majority areas.		
The allocation of houses by local councils favoured Catholics.		
The allocation of jobs in the civil service and local councils favoured Protestants.		
The British government forced O'Neill and his government to bring in reforms in housing and in local elections.		
O'Neill got support from the leading extreme unionist, Ian Paisley.		
O'Neill was succeeded as Prime Minister by Major James Chichester-Clark.		

5 Which of the following statements in relation to **Civil Rights and the end of Stormont** are true, and which are false? Tick the appropriate boxes.

	True	False
The Northern Ireland Civil Rights Association (NICRA) was formed because Catholics and nationalists were disappointed.		
The Northern Ireland Civil Rights Association (NICRA) was inspired by the civil rights movement in America.		
NICRA wanted 'One person, one vote' in local elections.		
NICRA wanted gerrymandering to be made legal.		

	True	False
NICRA wanted an end to discrimination in jobs and housing.		
NICRA leaders included Gerry Fitt, John Hume, Austin Currie and Brian Faulkner.		
NICRA organised marches in Derry and Belfast.		
In October 1968, a civil rights march in Derry was stopped by the RIC.		
The leaders of the civil rights march baton-charged the police.		
The British government forced O'Neill and his government to bring in reforms in housing and in local elections.		
Extreme unionists demanded that O'Neill, Prime Minister, should not give in to Catholics. O'Neill was forced to resign in 1969 when he got sick.		
Major violence was sparked off by the Protestant Apprentice Boys march in Derry.		
This march led to the Battle of the Bogside.		
Nationalists barricaded their area and resisted efforts by the Irish Army to enter the area.		
The British government sent in troops to protect the people of the Bogside.		
The people welcomed the soldiers with cups of tea.		
The Social Democratic and Labour Party (SDLP) was founded in 1970 and it brought together different unionist groups.		
The SDLP's first leader was Gerry Fitt, and he was succeeded by John Hume.		
The Provisional IRA was set up with the encouragement of members of the southern Irish government.		
Some Irish government money was used illegally to purchase weapons for the 'Provos'.		
The IRA launched a bombing campaign which resulted in the deaths of many civilians.		
The Unionist government of Brian Faulkner decided to bring in internment.		
Internment was a disastrous failure because the government had poor intelligence about UVF leaders, so many innocent people were arrested.		
On Bloody Sunday in 1972, British soldiers fired on an anti-internment march in Belfast.		
The British government decided to suspend the government and parliament of Northern Ireland and bring in direct rule from Stormont.		

❻ Identify each of the Northern Irish political leaders (1–8) and link them with the relevant comments (A–H).

Comments	
A	He founded the Democratic Unionist Party (DUP).
B	He was the first leader of the Social Democratic and Labour Party (SDLP).
C	He was the Prime Minister when Direct Rule from Westminster was brought in.
D	'I am an Orangeman first and a politician and member of this parliament afterwards.'
E	He has denied he was a member of the IRA.
F	'I appeal to loyalists, therefore, wherever possible to employ good Protestant lads and lassies.'
G	He met Sean Lemass twice.
H	He was one of the architects of the Northern Ireland peace process.

Leader's name	Comment
1	
2	
3	
4	
5	
6	
7	
8	

7 Discrimination in Northern Ireland – Using Key Ideas

Write your own account of Discrimination in Northern Ireland using the words under **Conflict with Catholics** and **Discrimination** p. 101, without referring to your textbook.

Make each point and develop it

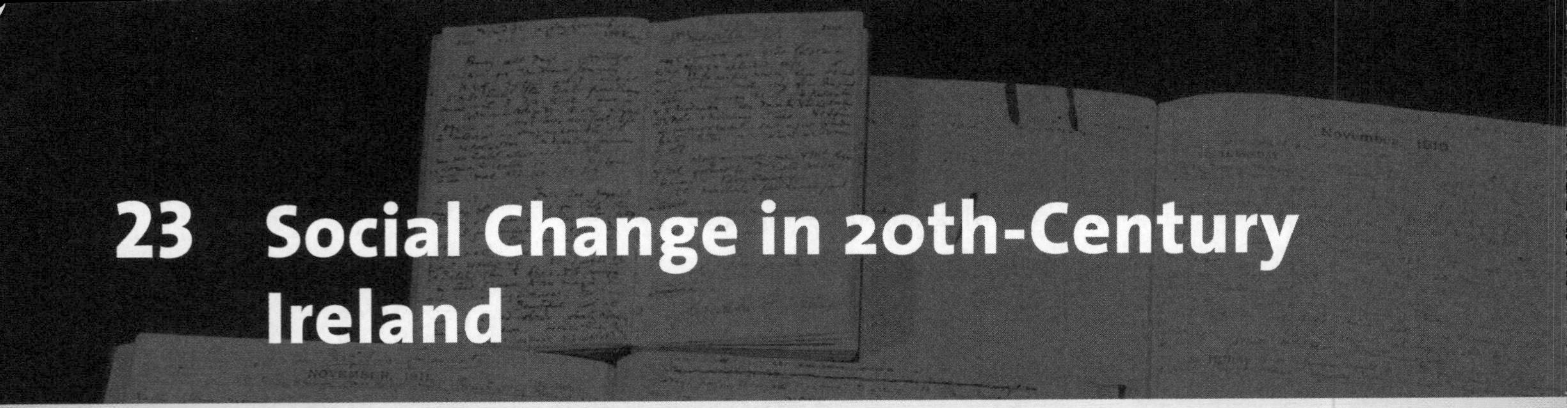

23 Social Change in 20th-Century Ireland

Key ideas

See the key ideas on pp. 321–2 of your textbook.

1 Fill in the spaces in the sentences below.

(i) In 1919 Countess Markievicz became the first female government m_____________ in Dáil Éireann.

(ii) The Irish Constitution of 1922 gave women over the age of 21 the right to v_____________.

(iii) In 1972 the Report of the Commission for the S_____________ of Women recommended ways to end inequality.

(iv) The marriage b_____________, which forced married women to give up jobs in the civil service after marriage, was lifted in 1973.

(v) The Employment E_____________ Act 1977 outlawed discrimination on the basis of gender or marital status.

(vi) Mary Robinson became the first woman P_____________ of Ireland in 1990.

2 These charts from the Central Statistics Office show change in people's working lives and an increase in the popularity of television. Study these graphs and answer the questions which follow.

☆ Numeracy

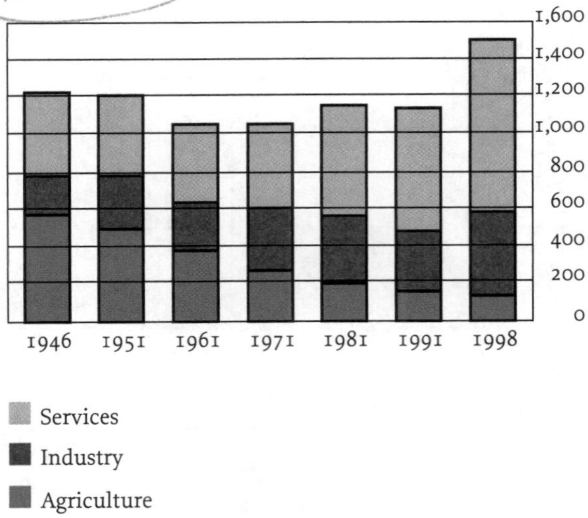

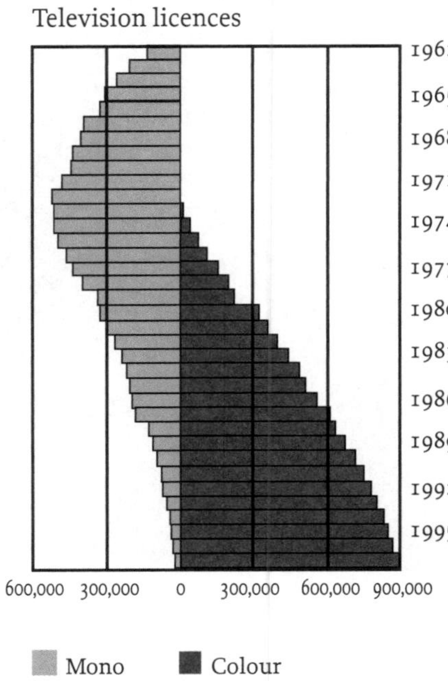

(From *That was Then, This is Now: Change in Ireland, 1949–1999*, edited by A. Redmond)

(i) To what extent did the numbers working in agriculture decrease between 1945 and 1998?

(ii) Give one reason for the decrease in the number of people working in agriculture since 1945.

(iii) Mention **two** consequences of the decrease in the number of people working in agriculture since 1945.

(iv) What was the main change in the purchase of television licences?

(v) Mention two consequences of the introduction of television since the 1960s.

3 Explain how each of the following sources would be useful in studying **social change** in Ireland. ✩ Historical skills

Church records

School roll-books

Census reports

Diaries

Apart from the above, identify 3 other types of primary source that a historian could use to find out about social history in 20th-century Ireland.

4 Census 1901 and 1911. ✩ Numeracy ✩ IT

Search the 1901 or 1911 Census (www.census.nationalarchives.ie/).

Browse by place. > Select census year (1901 or 1911). > Select County. > Then DED (District Electoral Division). > Select 1 Townland or Street known to you. > Make a summary of the information that you find. > How does that townland or street compare to today? (make a few general points)

Summary:

Comparison:

What does this tell you about social change?

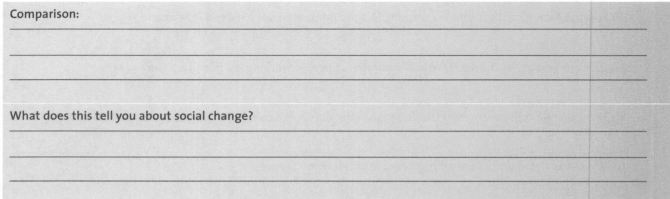

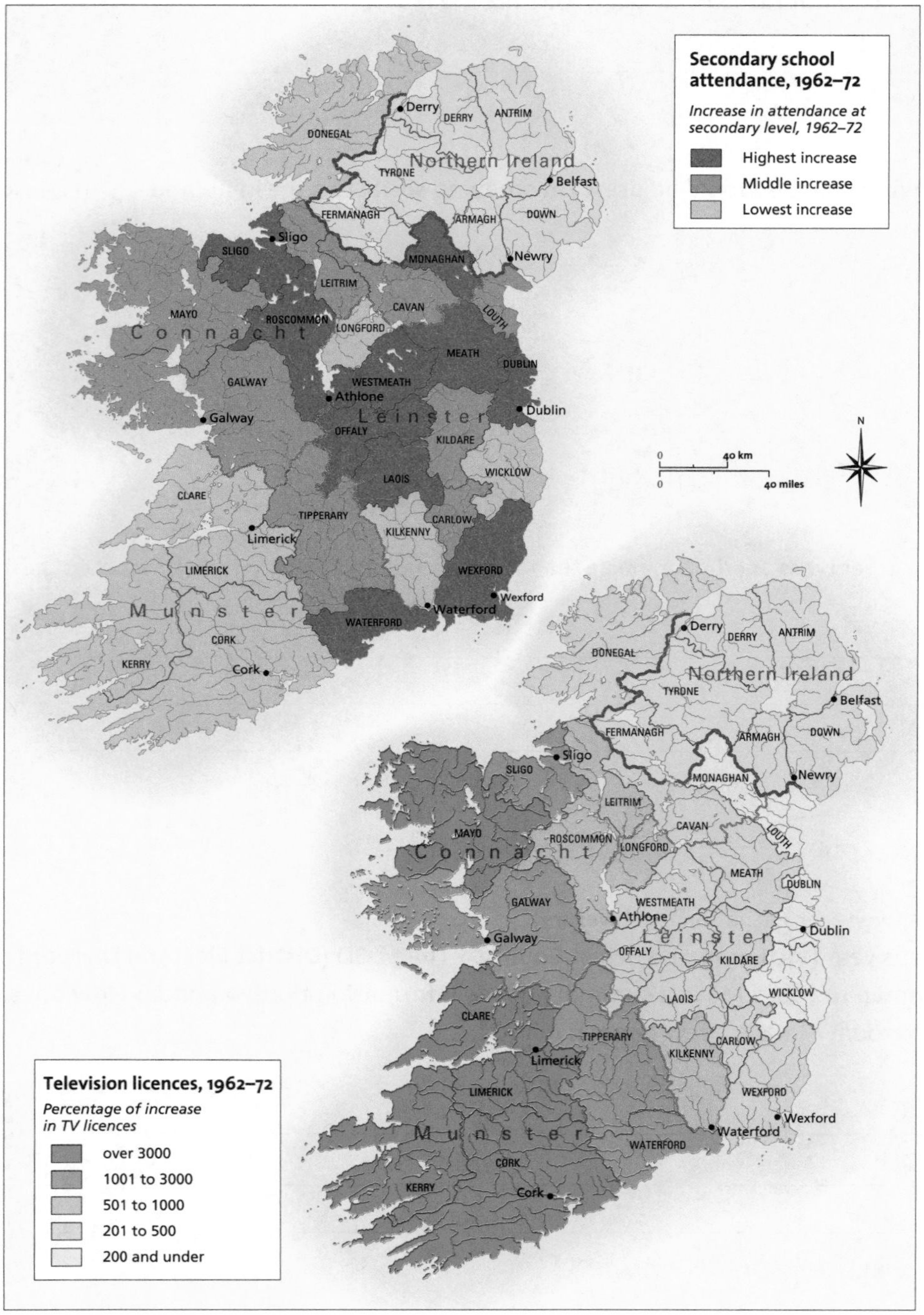

5 Study the map on secondary school attendance, 1962–72 on the previous page. ✭ Numeracy ✭ Historical analysis

(i) How many counties fitted into each category?

Highest increase ______ Middle increase ______ Lowest increase ______

(ii) Why was there an increase in secondary school attendance between 1962 and 1972?

______

______

(iii) Why did some counties show a greater increase than others?

______

______

6 Study the map on Television licences, 1962–72 on the previous page. ✭ Numeracy

(i) How many counties had an over 3000% increase in television licences between 1962 and 1972? ______

(ii) Where were these counties located?

______

(iii) What counties had the lowest percentage increase in television licences?

______

(iv) Why was there such a huge difference in the percentage increase between the counties in (i) compared to the counties in (iii)?

______

ANSWERING SOCIAL CHANGE QUESTIONS.

What did the Chief Examiner say about answering social change questions?

'In questions on social change, marks are only awarded for clearly stated **changes**. Candidates are expected to specify the changes that have occurred, showing **"the before and after"** of these changes and how the changes affected people's lives.'

'Candidates who performed poorly in Question 6 C (social change in 20th century Ireland) showed little grasp of the concept of social change and many could offer few practical meaningful examples of the phenomenon.' (2008)

EXAMPLES FROM 2012 JC MARKING SCHEME

The **Suggestions for answer** need to be written out as full sentences with examples to support what is written.

Q. Identify **three** major changes in housing since 1945.

Suggestions for answer: **Bungalows have replaced many farmhouses/Running water now in all houses/Various mod cons now found in every kitchen/Most houses now have central heating/Electricity was extended to houses in the countryside/Blocks of apartments have been built in the cities and most towns/Housing estates have grown up on the outskirts of almost every town, etc.**

Any **THREE** valid changes since 1945. 2 + 2 + 2 = 6M

Q. Give **three** major changes in road and motor transport since 1945.

Suggestions for answer: **Motorways have been built (joining the major cities)/Tolls have been introduced on a number of new roads/Many towns and villages now bypassed/Most families now own a car/Traffic congestion has become a major problem in the cities, etc.**

Internal gadgetry of the car, e.g., Sat nav, Bluetooth, etc. = 1SRS max. (2 marks max)

Any **THREE** valid changes since 1945. 2 + 2 + 2 = 6M

Write out one of the answers above

7. Write about five changes in each of the following since the 1940s. State the **'before and after'** in each change.

Agriculture

Rural housing

Urban housing

Work

Education

Transport

Communications

Women's lives

Sport and leisure

8. Construct a graph based on the following figures.
Use www.chartgo.com to construct your graph.

Numeracy

Year	Women's earnings as a % of men's
1969	47%
1979	58%
1989	61%
1998	66%
2006	86%
2011	94%

(*Source*: EU figures, www.ec.europa.eu/ireland/ireland_in_the_eu/impact_of_eu_on_irish_women/index_en.htm#1)

What conclusions can you draw from this graph?

24 Part 1: Peace and War in Europe, 1920–45

Key ideas – Versailles: The Tragic Peace

Treaty of Versailles – attitude of leaders – Wilson (US President), 14-point plan for peace, based on justice: each nation should have its own government (national self-determination), treat Germany fairly, set up League of Nations to settle disputes between countries. David Lloyd George (British Prime Minister) – pressure from people to treat Germany harshly, 'Make Germany Pay' slogan. Clemenceau (French President) – 'The Tiger' – wanted severe punishment of Germany – revenge for two defeats in war, also keep Germany weak. Treaty of Versailles – Germany had to sign. **Terms:** demilitarisation of Rhineland – no German army along River Rhine; Alsace–Lorraine returned to France; Germany lost territory to Poland – the Polish Corridor; union with Austria (Anschluss) forbidden; German army – 100,000 men, navy kept small, no submarines, no air force; war guilt clause – Germany to accept blame for causing World War I; reparations – Germany to pay £6.6 billion compensation to Allies; German reaction; very angry, resented war guilt clause and reparations. **Assessment:** terms too harsh on Germany; led to rise to power of Hitler, reparations payments caused conflict during 1920s.

League of Nations – aims – promote international co-operation to achieve peace; based on 'collective security' – each member responsible for security of other members; HQ in Geneva, Assembly – all decisions unanimous, Council of Ministers – also unanimous. Success? In small disputes, but bigger powers ignored the League – Japan in Manchuria, Italy in Ethiopia, Germany over Treaty of Versailles; League too weak – why? USA did not join, Germany and Russia only for a short time; decisions of Assembly and Council – unanimous – too slow; no army – only economic sanctions (boycotts) – broken easily.

1 Fill in the blank spaces in relation to the **Treaty of Versailles**.

President W______________ of the United States produced his F______________-Point Plan for peace in January 1918. He wanted 'the world to be made fit and safe to live in'. He believed that each nation with a common language, culture and history should govern itself (the principle of n______________ self-determination). He wanted Germany to be treated f______________. President Wilson suggested the formation of a L______________ of N______________.

David L______________ G______________, Prime Minister of Britain, said he would 'squeeze the German lemon until the pips squeak'.

President C______________ of France, known as 'the T______________', demanded severe punishment for Germany. The French people wanted r______________ for two German invasions of France, in 1870 and in 1914.

Germany had to accept the terms of the Treaty of Versailles: Germany had to accept Article 231, which laid the full b______________ for starting the war on German aggression.

Germany had to pay r______________ (compensation) of £6.6 billion for all damage done during the war. The Rhineland was d______________ – Germany was forbidden to have any armed forces stationed west of the

R______________ or within 50 kilometres to the east of the R______________. Alsace–Lorraine was returned to F______________; Germany lost territory to P______________. The 'P______________ C______________' – a narrow strip of land in Poland – separated Germany from East P______________, which was also part of Germany. The union of Germany and Austria (called *A*______________) was forbidden. The German army was reduced to 1______________ men. The navy was reduced to a small number of ships and no s______________ were allowed. Germany was not allowed to have an a______________ f______________.

Key ideas – Democracy and Dictatorship: The Rise of Fascism 1920–33

Democracy and dictatorship – rise of fascism; democracy – power of the people, freedom of speech; dictatorship – control by one man or party of press, radio, education, put down opposition – dictatorship spread in Europe during interwar years (1919–39), fascist dictators – Mussolini in Italy, Hitler in Germany. Fascism – opposition to socialists and communists, extreme nationalism, racism (especially anti-Semitism), against democracy, cult of leader.

Mussolini and Fascist Italy – Mussolini founded Fascio di Combattimento (fascist combat groups), symbol was fasces (bundle of rods). **Rise to power: effects of World War I** – half a million Italians killed, Italy failed to get land that was promised; rapid rise in prices (inflation), 2.5 million unemployed (demobilised soldiers) – strikes and riots. **Fear of communism** – socialists and communists grew in popularity; landlords, industrialists feared loss of property in a communist revolution. **Growth of Fascist Party** – Blackshirts attacked communists, increased membership, Mussolini a very good speaker, propagandist. **March on Rome** – Mussolini wanted fascists in government, threatened march on Rome, King Victor Emmanuel gave in – appointed Mussolini as prime minister.

Mussolini in power – establish dictatorship – passed law – party with most votes to get two-thirds of seats in parliament; murder of Matteoti – opposition left parliament. Rule by decree – Mussolini could make laws without parliament; censored press, radio, cinema; banned other parties; secret police (OVRA) crushed opposition. *Il Duce* – cult of personality – Mussolini photographed, 'Mussolini is always right'; propaganda – use of press, radio, cinema to glorify fascists. Youth – education used to indoctrinate youth, textbooks used to glorify Mussolini, youth organisations, e.g. Balila. Fascist changes – built *autostrada* (motorways), reclaimed Pontine Marshes – eliminate malaria, Battle of Grain – more grain, Battle of Births for more babies. Lateran Treaty – peace with the Pope – recognised Vatican state, Catholic religion official religion.

Mussolini's foreign policy – aims – recreate glories of Roman Empire, make Mediterranean Sea an 'Italian lake' (*Mare Nostrum* – 'Our Sea'); got 50 million lire compensation from Greece for death of Italian soldiers; image of peace-loving statesman – signed treaty guaranteeing border of France and Germany; also outlawing war; in 1930s more aggressive – expansion in Africa – invaded Ethiopia (Abyssinia) – easily won; League of Nations imposed sanctions on Italy; Mussolini supported by Hitler; agreed Rome–Berlin Axis with Hitler – allowed German takeover of Austria (Anschluss); signed Pact of Steel with Hitler – agreed to help each other in war. World War II – Mussolini did not join World War II at start – Italian army weak – joined when Germany invaded France; Italy defeated in North Africa, helped by Rommel; Allies invaded Italy – Mussolini deposed, held prisoner – rescued by Hitler; later captured and killed.

1 Fill in the information in the blank spaces below in relation to **Mussolini and Fascist Italy.**

(i) Mussolini's followers were known as the ______________.

(ii) After World War I, many Italians were unhappy with the Treaty of ______________.

(iii) Many businessmen feared the spread of ______________ and therefore supported fascism.

(iv) After the March on ______________, Mussolini was appointed Prime Minister of Italy.

(v) The ______________ Treaty, signed with the Pope in 1929, recognised the Vatican City as an independent state.

(vi) In 1935, the Italians invaded ______________.

❷ Match each Key Term with the corresponding explanation. (Literacy)

1	Blackshirts	A	Political belief of Mussolini in Italy
2	Fasces	B	Title used by Mussolini
3	Fascism	C	Name given to Mussolini's Fascist followers
4	Il Duce	D	Part of Mussolini's plan to get power in Italy
5	March on Rome	E	Symbol of axe and rods of Mussolini's Fascist Party

1	
2	
3	
4	
5	

❸ Explain the following terms in relation to **dictatorship and democracy.** (Literacy)

Communism	
Democracy	
Empire	
Imperialism	

❹ Fill in the boxes in relation to **Mussolini's Rise to Power** from the word list below.

Word List: Example of Russian Revolution; Half a million killed; governments fail to solve problems; 2.5 million soldiers demobilised; Failed to get promised land; Italian government and democracy blamed; Squadristi; 3 separate directions; Catholic Church feared 'godless' communism; King refused to use army; Blackshirts; Strikes & riots; Mussolini appointed PM; Italian pride hurt; Tortured opponents; Fascists demand to form government.

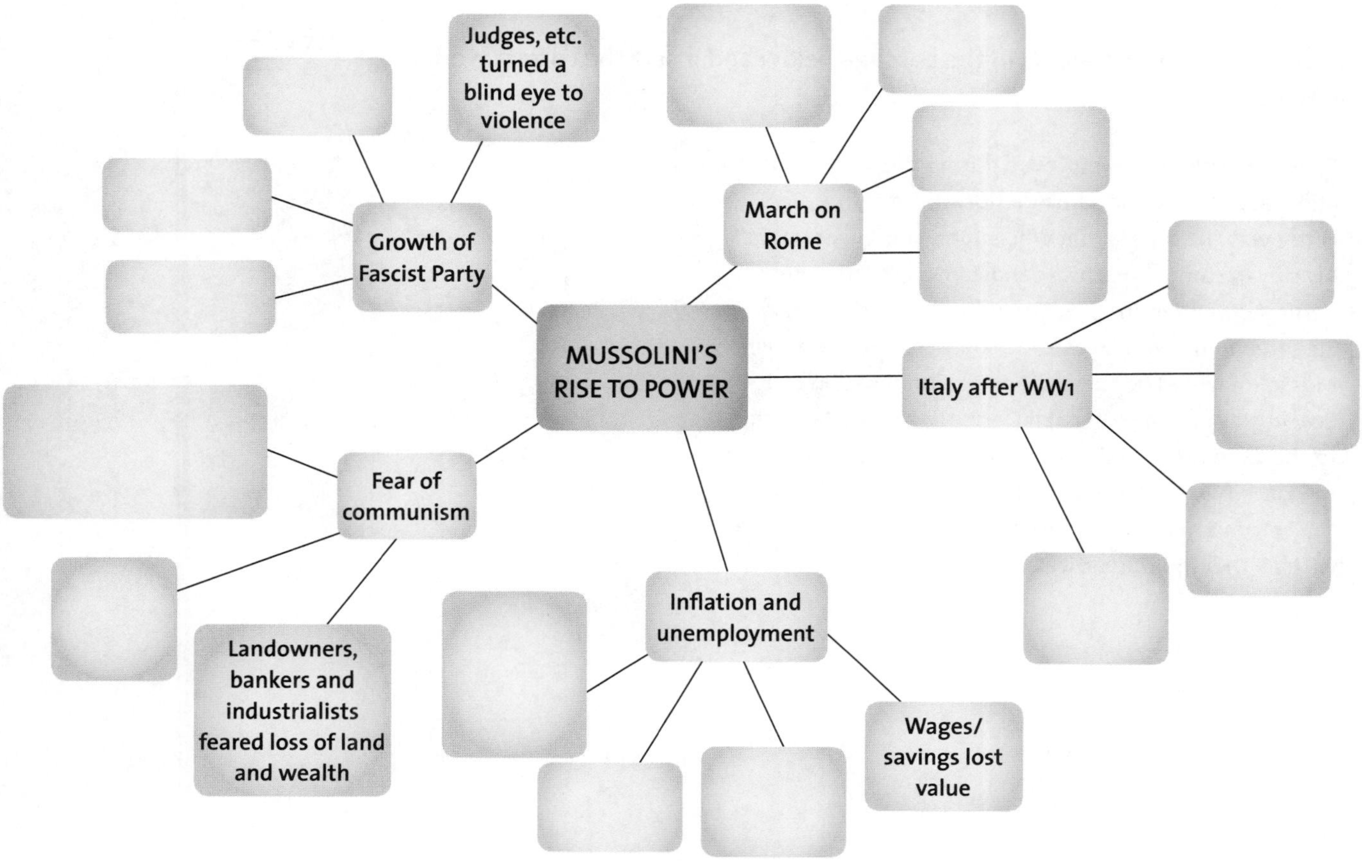

5 Fill in the blank spaces in relation to **Mussolini in Power.**

Mussolini had been legally appointed Prime Minister by the k__________, V__________ E__________

Mussolini's first task was to establish a d__________. In 1923, he passed the A__________ Law.

In the next election, Mussolini used his F__________ squads (s__________.) to beat up opponents and to ensure a m__________ in parliament. The o__________ parties withdrew from parliament in the A__________ Secession because of the murder of Giacomo M__________, a S__________ leader. Mussolini could 'r__________ by d__________', which allowed him to make laws without going through p__________. Mussolini used the secret police force (the O__________) to crush o__________. By now, he was d__________ of Italy. Mussolini used p__________ to create a cult of p__________. He used press, r__________ and c__________ to praise F__________ successes. Mussolini used slogans Such as 'B__________! O__________! F__________!' E__________ and youth organisations such as the B__________ were used to in__________ young boys and girls.

Mussolini improved the road system by building a__________. He reclaimed the P__________ M__________. He promoted the B__________ for G__________ to increase wheat production and the B__________ for B__________ to increase the population. He set up the C__________ State. He agreed the L__________ Treaty with the Pope. This ended a dispute which had gone on for s__________ years. He wanted to recreate the glories of the R__________ E__________ and make the Mediterranean Sea an I__________ lake (M__________ N__________).

6 Circle the **5 incorrect words** in the passage below and insert the correct words in the box on the side. ☆ Literacy

Relations with Hitler improved during the 1930s. Mussolini and Hitler shared the same democratic ideas, and Hitler was the only leader who supported Mussolini in his Libyan campaign. This friendship led to the Rome–Berlin Agreement in 1936. Mussolini and Hitler made an agreement over Czechoslovakia, according to which Mussolini would permit the German annexation of Czechoslovakia (*Anschluss*) if Germany did not lay claim to the German-speaking population in the South Tyrol. In 1939, the two leaders signed the Pact of Peace, in which they promised to help each other in war 'immediately and with all their military forces'.

1	
2	
3	
4	
5	

7 Focus Task ☆IT

Create a **Fakebook page for Benito Mussolini** at **www.classtools.net/FAKEBOOK.**

Use information from your textbook and from Benito Mussolini, spartacus-educational.com/2WWmussolini.htm.

Key ideas – Hitler and Nazi Germany

Background – Hitler, Austrian-born, fought for Germany in World War I, member of German Workers' Party after the war – later called National Socialist German Workers' Party (Nazi Party); wrote autobiography in prison, *Mein Kampf*. Hitler's ideas – union of all German speakers, abolish Treaty of Versailles, extra land in east for *lebensraum* (living space), Germans were Aryan race, pure, anti-Semitic (anti-Jewish).

Hitler's rise to power – weakness of Weimar Republic – blamed for defeat of Germany in World War I ('November criminals') and for Treaty of Versailles, frequent changes of government. Great Depression – spread from Wall Street, Germany had to repay loans to USA, unemployment rose to 6 million. Hitler's leadership – use democracy to defeat democracy; policies appeal to many groups – nationalism to everybody, anti-communism to businessmen and industrialists, revive the economy to industrialists and middle class.

Propaganda – Hitler an outstanding speaker, use of simple slogans; SA (Brownshirts) and SS (Blackshirts) attacked opposition, especially communists. Elections – Hitler and Nazi Party increased votes and seats in Reichstag; Hindenburg asked Hitler to become Chancellor.

Hitler in power – establish dictatorship – called general election, used SA and SS to beat opponents and win election; Reichstag fire: set by Dutch communist, blamed communists; Enabling Act gave Hitler power to rule by decree; banned other political parties; used Gestapo (secret police). Night of the Long Knives – Hitler used SS to kill off leaders of SA, especially Röhm because he threatened Hitler's power; Hindenburg died, Hitler combined Chancellor and President – became *Der Führer*. **Nazi propaganda** – Goebbels, Minister for Propaganda, controlled press, radio, cinema; newspaper editors had to be of Aryan descent; propaganda glorified Hitler – posters, his birthday, salute – Heil Hitler; Nuremberg Rallies, torchlight parades, Olympic Games in Berlin in 1936.

Youth – education used to glorify Hitler and Nazis, books rewritten, physical education emphasised; boys joined Hitler Youth, girls joined League of German Maidens.

Nazi economy – Battle for Work to eliminate unemployment; huge public works – build motorways (*autobahn*), houses, rearmament, motor cars – Volkswagen ('People's car').

Hitler and the Jews – banned Jews from civil service, journalism; Nuremberg Laws – Jews not German citizens, marriage between Jews and non-Jews banned, Jews must wear the Star of David. Night of the Broken Glass – German diplomat in Paris killed by Polish Jew; attack on Jewish businesses and synagogues in Germany, 90 Jews killed, some sent to concentration camps, Hitler fined Jews for damage; half German Jews emigrated, e.g. Einstein. Jews in World War II – the Final Solution – millions of Jews in Poland, Russia rounded up in ghettos, e.g. Warsaw, sent to concentration camps – Auschwitz, Treblinka; Final Solution – extermination of Jews – shooting, gassing – organised by Himmler and SS – 6 million killed; Nazis tried in Nuremberg Trials after war.

The Drift to War, 1933–39, the Causes of World War II – aims of Hitler's foreign policy – greater Germany, living space (*lebensraum*), destroy Treaty of Versailles; early success – Saar plebiscite – Saar agrees to join Germany; Hitler failed in first attempt to unite Austria with Germany. Destroying Versailles – conscription, submarine construction; remilitarisation of Rhineland – was not stopped by France or Britain; better relations with Mussolini – supported him in Abyssinia (Ethiopia), worked together in Spanish Civil War, Rome–Berlin Axis; united with Austria (Anschluss). Policy of appeasement – British and French policy – give in to Hitler's demands to prevent a world war; followed by Chamberlain (British Prime Minister); Germany harshly treated by Treaty of Versailles; French built Maginot Line; Hitler demands Sudetenland – German-speaking part of Czechoslovakia; war threatened. Munich Conference – Hitler, Chamberlain, Daladier (France), Mussolini gives Sudetenland to Hitler; took rest of country six months later; Britain changes policy of appeasement – getting ready for war; Nazi–Soviet Pact – 10-year non-aggression pact, agreed to divide Poland between them; Pact surprised everybody; Hitler demanded Polish Corridor – Poland refused, war threatened; Britain and France backed Poland, Hitler ordered attack, World War II began.

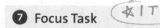

1 Fill in the information in the blank spaces in relation to **Hitler and Nazi Germany**.

(i) President ______________ appointed Hitler as Chancellor (Prime Minister) of Germany.

(ii) The secret police, the ______________ was established to put down opposition.

(iii) Ernst Rohm and other political opponents were killed by the SS on the Night ______________________________.

(iv) In 1936 German troops entered the __________________________.

(v) In the same year Hitler and ______________ formed an alliance known as the Rome–Berlin Axis.

(vi) In March 1938, Germany took over Austria in an event known as the ______________.

(vii) At the Munich Conference the ______________ was given to Germany.

(viii) The rest of ______________ was occupied by Germany in March 1939.

(ix) The British Prime Minister, Neville Chamberlain, believed in a foreign policy known as ______________.

2 Match each Key Term with the corresponding explanation. (Literacy)

1	Enabling Act	A	Plan to exterminate the Jews
2	Führer	B	More controls on the Jews
3	Night of the Crystal Glass	C	Power to rule without asking parliament
4	Night of the Long Knives	D	Living space in Eastern Europe
5	Lebensraum	E	Leader
6	Final Solution	F	Gave all power to Hitler
7	Rule by decree	G	Attack on Jewish businesses and synagogues
8	Nuremberg Laws	H	Murders of SA leaders by SS

1	
2	
3	
4	
5	
6	
7	
8	

3 Explain these Key Terms in relation to **Nazi Germany**. (Literacy)

Appeasement	
Brownshirts	
Communism	
Democracy	
Swastika	

4 Fill in the information in the boxes in relation to **Hitler's Rise to Power** from the word list below.

Word List: Failure of Munich Putsch; Blamed for defeat of Germany in WWI; Weimar blamed; American loans; Democracy blamed; Frequent changes of government; Blamed for Treaty of Versailles; Outstanding speaker; Nationalism & opposition to Treaty of Versailles; Uniforms, right-arm salute, swastika; Revive the economy; November Criminals; Intimidated opponents; Simple slogans; Brownshirts, Blackshirts; Appealed to different groups; Anti-communism; Blame for Germany's troubles.

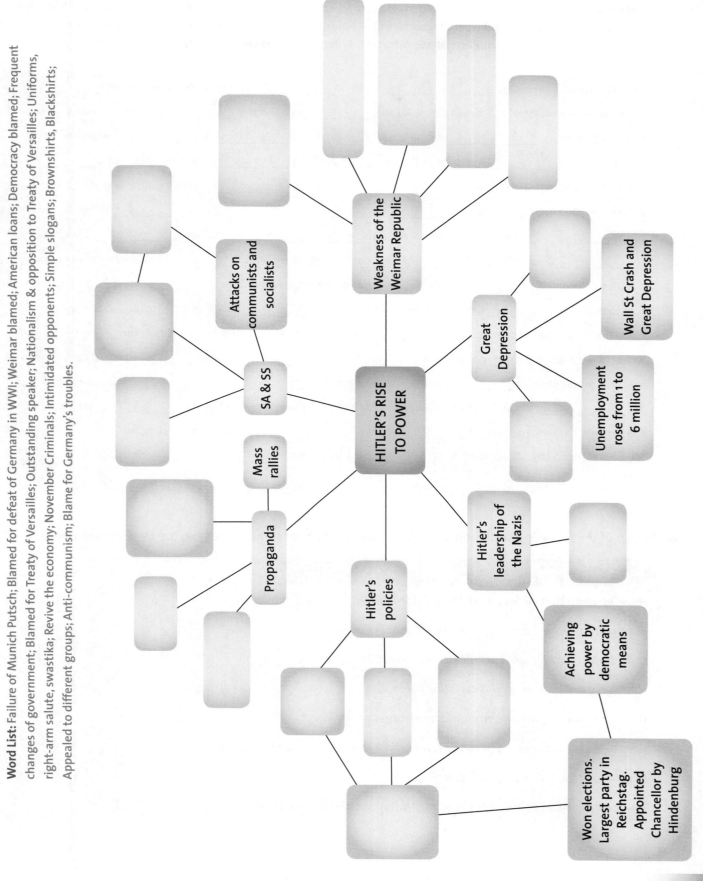

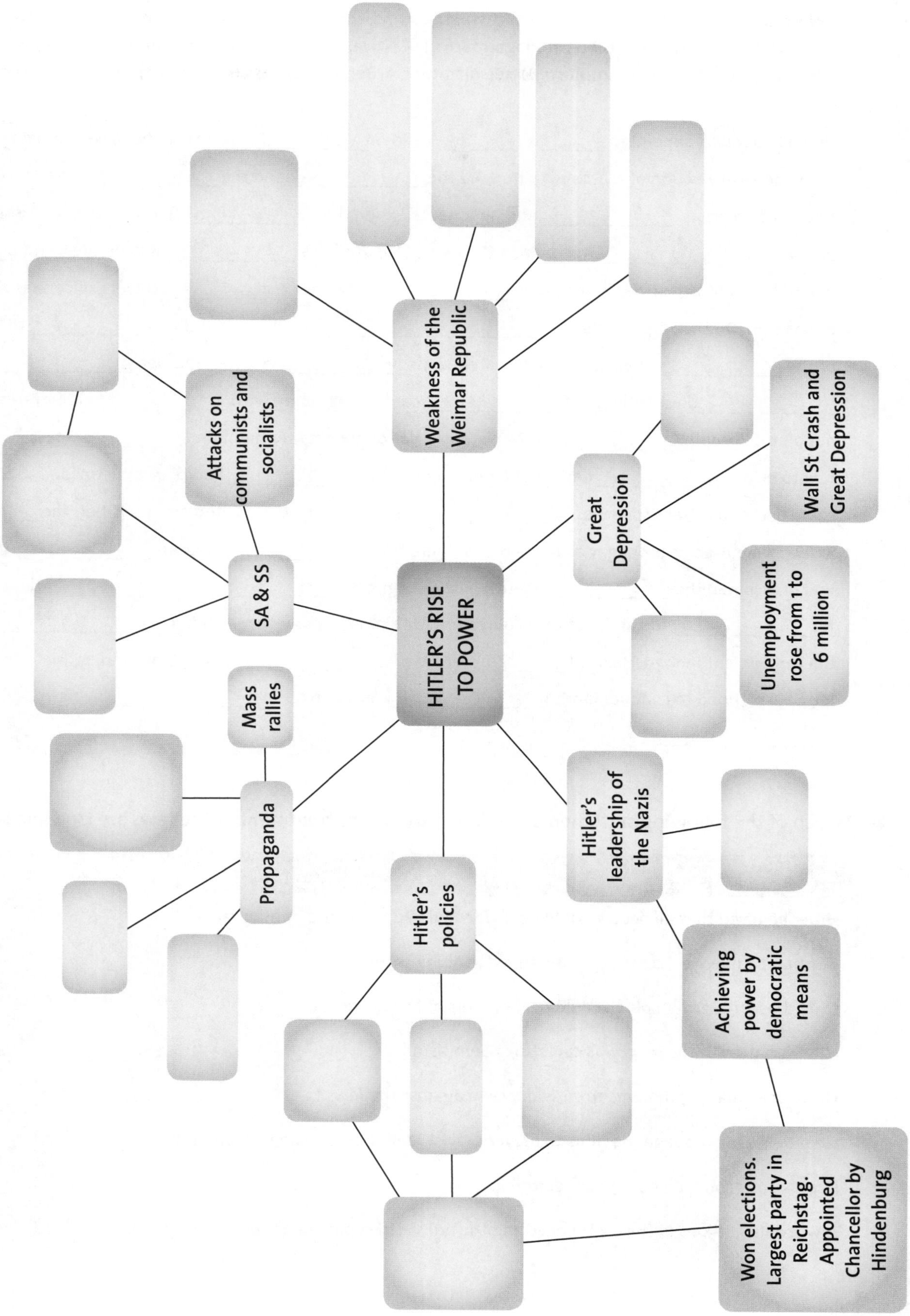

5 Fill in the information in relation to **Hitler in Power** from the word list below.

Word List: Aryan; German Maidens; Reichstag; Gestapo; Long Knives; Führer; public; Olympic; Goebbels; Chancellor; materials; rearmament; decree; Propaganda; Hitler; power; voters; Hindenburg; Nuremberg; six; concentration; People's; lebensraum; communists; Work; dictator; SA; Berlin; Eastern; Enabling Act; SS; Dachau; Nazi; cult.

When Hitler was appointed ______________ by President ______________, he set about becoming a ______________. In the general election of March 1933, he used the ______________ and the ______________ as an auxiliary police force. They beat up ______________ and opponents. When the ______________ (parliament) was set on fire, he blamed the ______________ and banned their Party. He used the ______________ Act to rule by ______________. He banned all political parties except the ______________ Party. The______________, secret police, was used to put down opposition. On the Night of the ______________ ______________, Hitler used the ______________ to kill the leadership of the ______________ because they threatened his______________. He became Der ______________ after President ______________ died. Hitler built ______________ camps, beginning with ______________, to imprison opponents. He appointed Joseph ______________ as Minister for National Enlightenment and ______________. Newspaper editors had to be of ______________ descent. Cheap radios – the ______________ Radio – were provided so that people could listen to Hitler's speeches. A ______________ of personality was created around Hitler. The ______________ Rallies were used as propaganda occasions, as were the ______________ Games in ______________ in 1936. Boys and girls joined the ______________ Youth or the League of ______________ ______________. Hitler used the Battle for ______________ to eliminate unemployment. Unemployment was reduced from ______________ million to no unemployment in 1939. He used ______________ works, ______________ and the expanding motor industry to provide jobs. He planned to conquer lands in ______________ Europe to obtain ______________ (living space) for food and raw ______________.

6 Which of the following statements in relation to **Hitler's treatment of the Jews** are true and which are false?

	True	False
Hitler believed that all people could be divided into superior and inferior races.		
German people were a racially pure, superior Alpha people.		
Only those of German blood could be members of the German nation.		
Hitler's hatred of the Jews was called anti-Semitism.		
Hitler used maths problems to spread racism against the Jews.		
Goebbels used propaganda films to prevent racist feeling spreading in Germany.		
Only Aryans could be newspaper editors.		
Jews could get jobs in the civil service and the universities provided they spoke German.		

	True	False
In the Nuremberg Laws, Jews were deprived of German citizenship if they were born outside of Germany.		
Jews had to wear the Star of Saul.		
Marriage between Jews and non-Jews was allowed if they paid Hitler money.		
The Night of Broken Glass was also known as Kristallnacht.		
That night Jewish shops and synagogues were not attacked if they put a swastika on the door.		
That night about ninety Jews were killed.		
Hitler insisted that the Jewish community had to pay for the damage to their own buildings.		
By 1939, all of Germany's 600,000 Jews had emigrated.		
Einstein, the great scientist, was one of the Jews who emigrated to other countries.		
In World War II, Jews were rounded up and contained in ghettos such as that in Warsaw.		
The Nazis put into action their 'Final Solution', which was the extermination of the Jews.		
Hitler had concentration camps such as Auschwitz and extermination camps such as Dachau.		
6 million European Jews were killed in the Holocaust.		

7 How *useful* is each of these sources for studying the Nazi treatment of the Jews? (☆ Historical skills) (☆ IT)

SOURCE A

Mob law rules

Mob law ruled in Berlin throughout the afternoon and evening as hordes of hooligans took part in an orgy of destruction. I have never seen an anti-Jewish outbreak as sickening as this. I saw fashionably dressed women clapping their hands and screaming with glee while respectable mothers held up their babies to see the 'fun'. No attempt was made by the police to stop the rioters.

(*Source*: The *Daily Telegraph*, 12 November, 1938)

SOURCE B

Revenge for murder by a Jew

The death of a loyal party member by the Jewish murderer has aroused spontaneous anti-Jewish demonstrations throughout the Reich. In many places, Jewish shops have been smashed. The synagogues, from which teachings hostile to the State and People are spread, have been set on fire. Well done to those Germans who have ensured revenge for the murder of an innocent German.

(*Source: Der Stürmer*, 10 November, 1938)

(i) Google each of the newspaper titles and read about the background of the newspapers.

How useful are the sources?

(ii) Source A: ______________________________

____

(iii) Source B: ______________________________

____

How reliable are the sources?

(iv) ______________________________

____

8 Identify each of the European political leaders (1–10) and link them with the relevant comments (A–J).

1

2

3

4

5

6

7

8

9
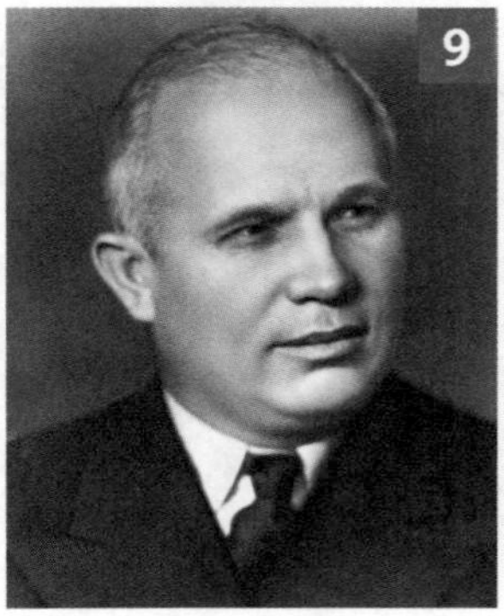

10

You may need to check online for these comments

Comments	
A	'That propaganda is good which leads to success, and that is bad which fails to achieve the desired result.'
B	'If outvoting them takes longer than outshooting them, at least the results will be guaranteed by their own Constitution.'
C	'Never in the field of human conflict was so much owed by so many to so few.'
D	'Without perestroika, the Cold War simply would not have ended.'
E	'What is our task? To make Britain a fit country for heroes to live in.'
F	'How horrible, fantastic, incredible, it is that we should be digging trenches and trying on gas-masks here because of a quarrel in a faraway country between people of whom we know nothing.'
G	'The decision, therefore, lies here in the East; here must the Russian enemy, this people numbering two hundred million Russians, be destroyed on the battlefield and person by person, and made to bleed to death.'
H	'The world must be made safe for democracy.'
I	'It is better to live one day as a lion than 100 years as a sheep.'
J	'Politicians are the same all over. They promise to build a bridge even where there is no river.'

Leader's name	Comment
1	
2	
3	
4	
5	
6	
7	
8	
9	
10	

9 The events A to F below all relate to **Nazi Foreign Policy, 1933–39**. Number the events in chronological order, starting with the event which happened first.

☆ Numeracy

A. Anschluss with Austria	A
B. Nazi–Soviet Pact	B
C. Remilitarisation of Rhineland	C
D. Germany withdraws from the League of Nations	D
E. Munich Conference	E
F. Rome–Berlin Axis	F

10 Match up the beginning and end of these sentences on **Hitler's Foreign Policy and the drift to World War II.**

☆ Historical skills

1	He wanted to create a Greater Germany (*Grossdeutschland*)	A	rather than to stay with France.
2	He intended to create an empire	B	did not want a repetition of the horrors of World War I.
3	He wanted to destroy	C	when Mussolini, the Italian leader, opposed him.
4	In the Saar plebiscite the people of the Saar voted to become part of Germany	D	by introducing conscription and beginning submarine construction.
5	His first attempt at uniting Austria with Germany (*Anschluss*) failed	E	by sending German troops to reoccupy (remilitarise) the Rhineland.
6	He broke the Treaty of Versailles.	F	the Treaty of Versailles.
7	Hitler took a great gamble	G	it allowed Hitler to proceed with the annexation of Austria.
8	Hitler and Mussolini came closer together because of	H	by uniting all German-speaking people who lived in countries outside the German border.
9	The Rome–Berlin Axis was important because	I	that if they gave in to Hitler's demands, they would prevent war.
10	The British government followed a policy of appeasement, believing it	J	that would last 1,000 years, the Third Reich.
11	The Polish Corridor	K	met at the Munich Conference.
12	Neville Chamberlain, the British Prime Minister, believed	L	the Italian invasion of Abyssinia (Ethiopia) and the Spanish Civil War.
13	France built the Maginot Line because it believed that	M	because it was following a policy of isolation.

1	
2	
3	
4	
5	
6	
7	
8	
9	
10	
11	
12	
13	
14	
15	
16	

14	Hitler, Chamberlain, Mussolini and Daladier (France)	N	so they signed the Nazi–Soviet Pact in 1939.
15	The United States was not prepared to help either Britain or France,	O	this defensive line would prevent a German attack.
16	Hitler and Stalin, the leader of the Soviet Union, did not want to fight each other yet,	P	was the only piece of land taken from Germany at Versailles that Hitler had yet to recover.

11 Identify each of the areas numbered 1 to 8.

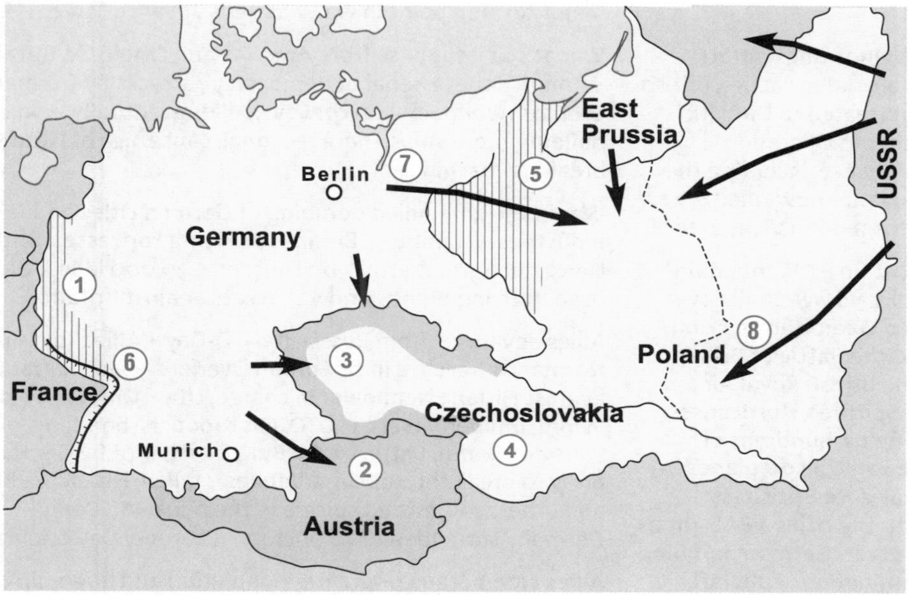

1.

2.

3.

4.

5.

6. What is the name of the line?

7. What does the arrow indicate?

8. What does the arrow indicate?

9. What does this map show about the expansion of Hitler's Germany?

Key ideas – World War II in Europe

German victories, 1939–42 – invasion of Poland, use of blitzkrieg (lightning war) tactics – German Luftwaffe attack to gain control of the air, German panzer (tanks) attack, infantry capture weakened Polish army; defeated Poland in 5 weeks; divided with Soviet Russia. Phoney War – no fighting over winter – only at sea – German ships attacked Allied shipping – sinking of German battleship, *Admiral Graf Spee*. Denmark and Norway – Denmark in one day, Norway conquered to protect iron ore supplies from Sweden in winter; Quisling put in charge of Norway by Germans.

Invasion of France – Germans avoid Maginot Line – attack through Ardennes Mountains – use of blitzkrieg tactics; British and French armies cut off in Belgium; retreated to Dunkirk – 300,000 soldiers evacuated from beaches in Operation Dynamo; Germans captured the rest of France, including the Maginot Line – Mussolini joined war – France now ruled directly by Germans or by puppet government in Vichy France.

Operation Sea Lion and the Battle of Britain – Chamberlain replaced as Prime Minister by Churchill; said 'We shall never surrender'; German invasion plan called Operation Sea Lion; had to get control of the air first, led to the Battle of Britain between the German Luftwaffe and the British Royal Air Force; Messerschmitts, Stukas against Spitfires, Hurricanes; Germans attack radar stations and airfields, hundreds of aircraft attack each day – in Day of the Eagle, 1,500 planes attacked; RAF stretched to limits – radar gave British an advantage; Germans switched attack to the cities – RAF got a breather – Hitler postponed invasion. **Blitz** – German bombing of British cities – London, Coventry, Birmingham – aircraft factories, power stations, ports – people evacuated to countryside, some returned – took shelter in Underground; will to resist; Churchill gave leadership; 40,000 killed; Blitz ended when Hitler decided to invade Russia. America brought into the war by Japanese attack on Pearl Harbor; major turning point.

Operation Barbarossa – German invasion plan for Russia – to defeat communism, to create lebensraum; attack on 22 June 1941; three-pronged attack – Leningrad, Moscow, Kiev – blitzkrieg tactics – rapid advance over flat countryside – Stalin called on Russians to resist in 'Great Patriotic War'; used scorched earth tactics (burning crops, destroying bridges); moved war industry beyond the Ural Mountains; winter cold halted Germans before Leningrad and Moscow; main attack next year (1942) was towards Stalingrad and oil fields of Caucasus; Russians fight street by street to defend Stalingrad, supplies across River Volga; cut off German army who resisted over winter but had to surrender. **Battle of Stalingrad** – a major turning point in war; Russians advance towards Berlin.

War at sea – supplies from America and Empire to Britain – America the 'arsenal of democracy'; attacks by German U-boats (wolfpacks) on convoys; Allies eventually won by building more ships, more reconnaissance, use of Ultra – code-breaking machine.

War in the air – Allied bombing of German cities and industries – Hamburg, Berlin – US Flying Fortresses, British Lancasters; worst attack on Dresden – 30,000 killed; Germans used V1 flying bombs and V2 rockets against Britain.

Allies advance – from Russia, Italy; D-Day – Allied invasion of Normandy beaches in Operation Overlord – second front against Hitler; Eisenhower in charge; Utah, Omaha, Gold, Juno, Sword; mulberry piers, PLUTO, paratroopers, bombing, on to Paris and Berlin; Battle of the Bulge – attempt by German army to break through in Ardennes – failed; Hitler, Eva Braun and others committed suicide in the bunker in Berlin; Germany surrendered; VE (Victory in Europe) Day celebrated.

Allies won because – greater population and larger armies; American wealth – huge production of airplanes and tanks; oil production greater; key victories to the Allies – Battle of Britain, Battle of Stalingrad, El Alamein in North Africa, war at sea.

Results – death – 55 million civilians and soldiers killed; destruction of cities, industries; war trials at Nuremberg; Germany divided between Britain, USA, France and Soviet Union (Russia); Cold War after the war; European supremacy ended; US and USSR (Russia), superpowers.

1 Match each item in Column A with the corresponding item in Column B. ☆ Literacy

Column A		Column B	
1	Blitzkrieg	A	German invasion of the USSR
2	Phoney War	B	Nazi plan to invade Britain
3	Dunkirk	C	USA provides Britain with military materials
4	Operation Sea Lion	D	Swift mechanised, military attack
5	Lend-Lease	E	British and French troops evacuated to England
6	Operation Barbarossa	F	The winter of 1939–40

1	
2	
3	
4	
5	
6	

2 Explain each of the following Key Terms in relation to **World War II.** ☆ Literacy

Battle of Britain	
Blitz	
Luftwaffe	
Panzer	
RAF	
Scorched earth policy	
U-boat	

3 Which of the following statements on **Early German victories, 1939–1941,** are true, and which are false? Tick the appropriate box.

	True	False
The German army used new war tactics against Poland.		
Blitzkrieg tactics, or 'lightning war', were used against France and Russia.		
The Soviet Union invaded from the east when Finland was largely defeated.		
The 'Phoney War' was a period over the winter of 1939 when enemy troops faced each other across the Franco-Polish border but did not fight.		
Iron ore from neutral Sweden was shipped to Germany through Norway during the winter.		
Hitler wanted to ensure that the German ore supply would be secure for the rest of the war so he invaded Sweden.		
In Norway, German paratroopers were also dropped to control bridges, airports and radio stations.		
Vidkun Quisling, a Norwegian sympathetic to Hitler, was made Minister-President of Norway.		
French generals assumed that Hitler would follow the German plans of World War I and attack through Switzerland.		
In Operation Dynamo, Britain sent all available boats to rescue the troops from the beaches of Dunkirk.		
The Maginot Line was captured from behind.		
Vichy France was ruled by a French government under German control.		
Neville Chamberlain replaced Winston Churchill as Prime Minister.		

	True	False
Hitler's invasion plan of Britain was codenamed Operation Green.		
The Spitfires, Hurricanes and Heinkels defended Britain.		
The Battle of Britain was Hitler's first defeat.		
During the Blitz people in London slept in the Underground each night.		
Hitler stopped the Blitz when he needed the planes for the invasion of Italy in June, 1941.		
Britain was able to continue the fight against Hitler with help from the USA through the Lend-Lease scheme.		

4. Fill in the blank spaces in this account of the **Invasion of the Soviet Union**.

Hitler looked on C______________ R______________ as his greatest enemy, and he planned to destroy it. He also wanted to create l______________ (living space) in Eastern Europe. He ordered the German army to attack Russia on 22 June 1941 in Operation B______________.

Hitler again used blitzkrieg tactics in a t______________-pronged attack directed towards the important Soviet cities of L______________, Moscow and K______________. The L______________ took control of the air, and German tanks and i______________ moved quickly into Russia as the Soviet army retreated. However, the Russian leader, S______________, called on Russians to fight the 'G______________. P______________ War' against Germany. Stalin moved heavy industry east of the U______________ Mountains, so that they could continue to produce tanks, planes and weapons.

As the Russians retreated, they used a s______________ earth policy. They destroyed crops and c______________ lines so that the Germans could not use them. Then Hitler's early progress was halted by the Russian winter of 1941–42. Lorries, tanks and airplanes seized up, and soldiers froze to death on duty. In 1942, Hitler's armies advanced towards S______________ and the oil fields of the C______________. Their advance was stopped at the Battle of S______________. The German army, under von P______________, fought vicious street battles with the Russian army defending the city. Russian reinforcements and supplies were ferried across the River V______________ each night to hold on to the city. S______________ insisted the city must not be lost. The Russians then attacked from the sides in a p______________ movement and cut off the German army in the city from their supplies. Eventually, over ______________ German soldiers were forced to surrender in February 1943.

5 Match up the beginning and end of these sentences on **D-Day, June, 1944.** ✩ Historical skills

1	Stalin demanded that the Allies open	A	was code-named Operation Overlord.
2	The invasion of the continent of Europe on D-Day, 6 June 1944,	B	because of its beaches, shallow water and closeness to Britain.
3	The Allies selected France's Normandy coast for their invasion	C	code-named Utah, Omaha, Gold, Juno and Sword.
4	General Eisenhower	D	a 'second front' in the west.
5	The Allies landed at five beaches	E	to bring in tanks and trucks.
6	Allied troops set up artificial harbours (called mulberry piers)	F	was the commander of the D-Day operations.

1	
2	
3	
4	
5	
6	

6 Insert the following events from World War II in the timeline below. ✩ Chronology

A. The invasion of Poland
B. Operation Barbarossa begins
C. The invasion of Norway
D. The invasion of Belgium, Holland and France
E. Hitler's suicide
F. The Battle of Britain
G. The Blitz
H. America enters the war
I. Operation Overlord
J. Battle of Stalingrad
K. Bombing of Hiroshima

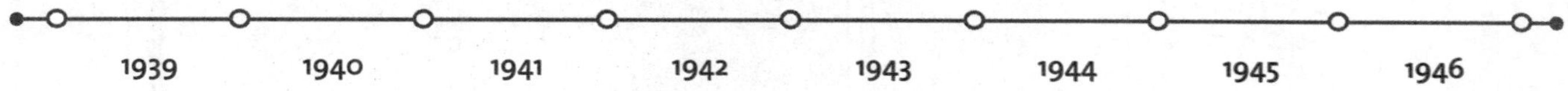

❼ Why Germany lost World War II – Develop your own Mind Map (see p. 139) ✯ Historical skills

Use your textbook and the internet to develop your own mind map on why Germany lost World War II.

WHY GERMANY LOST WWII

25 Part 2: The Rise of the Superpowers, 1945–91

Key ideas

Cold War – A time of tension and hostility between USA and USSR – two superpowers. **Causes** – political differences – communism versus capitalism; disagreements during World War II; disagreements after the war; Truman Doctrine and Marshall Plan.

Major events – Berlin Blockade, Korean War, Cuban Missile Crisis.

1. Write your own account of the **Berlin Blockade** using all the words/phrases here: four occupied zones; four sectors; condition of post-war Germany; Soviet Union; Allied powers – USA, Britain, France; huge reparations; revive German economy; democratic government; Marshall Plan; new currency; cut off road, rail and canal links; East Berlin; West Berlin; 2.5 million West Berliners; three air corridors; Operation Vittles; 8,000 tons of cargo; rationing; industry; spirit of the people; leave Berlin or drop currency plans; blockade lifted.

Revising Modern Europe

Literacy

ACROSS

3 Conference between Hitler, Mussolini, Chamberlain and Daladier.
6 German tank movement in World War II.
12 Nazi secret police.
13 Hated by Hitler.
17 Code-name for D-Day.
20 Overthrow of government by force.
21 Marshes drained by Mussolini.
24 Nazi extermination camp.
27 British Prime Minister at beginning of World War II.
29 US President at the start of the Cold War.
30 Mussolini marched here.
33 German defensive line.
34 Soviet leader during the Cuban Missile Crisis.
36 Applied to the Rhineland in the Treaty of Versailles.
37 Hitler as leader.
39 Code-name for German invasion of the Soviet Union.
42 German strategy of rapid movement in World War II.
43 US plan to revive Europe after World War II.
44 Victory in Europe.
45 Mussolini as leader.
46 Piers used after D-Day.
47 First major war of the Cold War.

DOWN

1 Curtain that divided Europe between East and West.
2 Code-name for Berlin Airlift.
4 US spyplane during the Cold War.
5 US President during the Cuban Missile Crisis.
7 Agreement between Mussolini and the Pope.
8 Victory in Japan.
9 Pipeline under the ocean.
10 German city heavily bombed in World War II.
11 U-boats together.
14 The day 1,500 German planes attacked Britain during the Battle of Britain.
15 Weimar government called criminals.
16 German-speaking area of Czechoslovakia.
18 Battle in Soviet Union, a turning point in World War II.
19 Hatred of the Jews.
22 He said, 'We shall never surrender'.
23 Nickname for Clemenceau, leader of France.
25 Polish territory separating Germany from East Prussia.
26 Union of Germany and Austria.
28 British policy towards Germany in 1930s.
31 French defensive line.
32 Code-breaking machine.
35 Minister of Propaganda.
38 Another British city, apart from London, bombed during the Blitz.
40 A Normandy beach in D-Day.
41 Mussolini youth organisation.
42 German bombing campaign of Britain.
44 Part of France ruled by French government who favoured the Nazis.

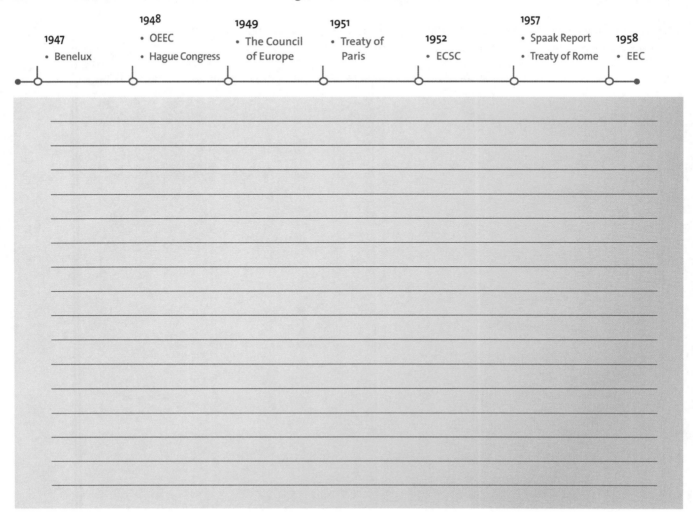

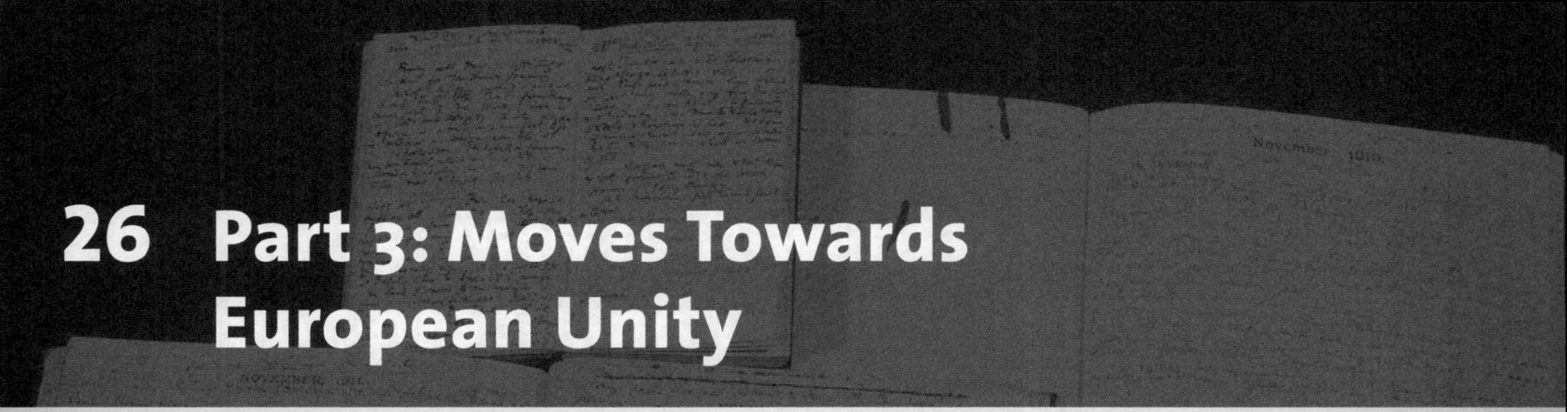

26 Part 3: Moves Towards European Unity

Key ideas

Reasons for European unity – wars in Europe; combine in order to compete against US and USSR; fear of spread of communism; control Germany within Europe; leaders such as Churchill, Schuman, de Gasperi and Adenauer encouraged it; supported by USA and Britain.

Steps to European unity – Benelux Treaty; OEEC – Organisation for European Economic Co-operation; Council of Europe; Schuman Plan – Treaty of Paris – ECSC (European Coal and Steel Community); Treaty of Rome and foundation of EEC (European Economic Community); a common market, common policies; enlargement with Britain, Ireland and Denmark; further enlargements.

1 Use this timeline to write an account of the **origins and foundation of the EEC**.

1947
- Benelux

1948
- OEEC
- Hague Congress

1949
- The Council of Europe

1951
- Treaty of Paris

1952
- ECSC

1957
- Spaak Report
- Treaty of Rome

1958
- EEC

27 Part 4: Asian Nationalism after 1945 – Gandhi and Indian Independence

Key ideas

Colonial background – British Empire – India, one of largest parts; movement for independence led by Indian National Congress Party.

Gandhi's role – non-violence; impact of World War II; Britain weakened – independence after war – conflict between Hindus and Muslims – other problems after independence; general move towards independence by African and Asian countries after war.

1 Focus Task

Create a **Fakebook page for Mahatma Gandhi** at www.classtools.net/**FAKEBOOK.**
Concentrate on his life and work from 1945 to his death.

Use information from your textbook and from the Complete Site on Mahatma Gandhi, www.mkgandhi.org/.

Active History

School History Society

Form your own School History Society

- History Noticeboard
- Lunchtime meetings
- Local History
- YouTube clips for discussion
- History Newsletter
- History on TV
- History Debates
- And more...
- Topics for Discussion
- Historical origins
- How to Research Family History
- Invite speakers from school or outside

Do Your Own Mind Maps for Revision

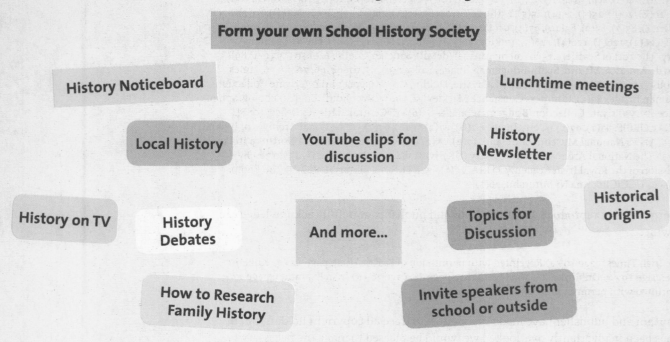

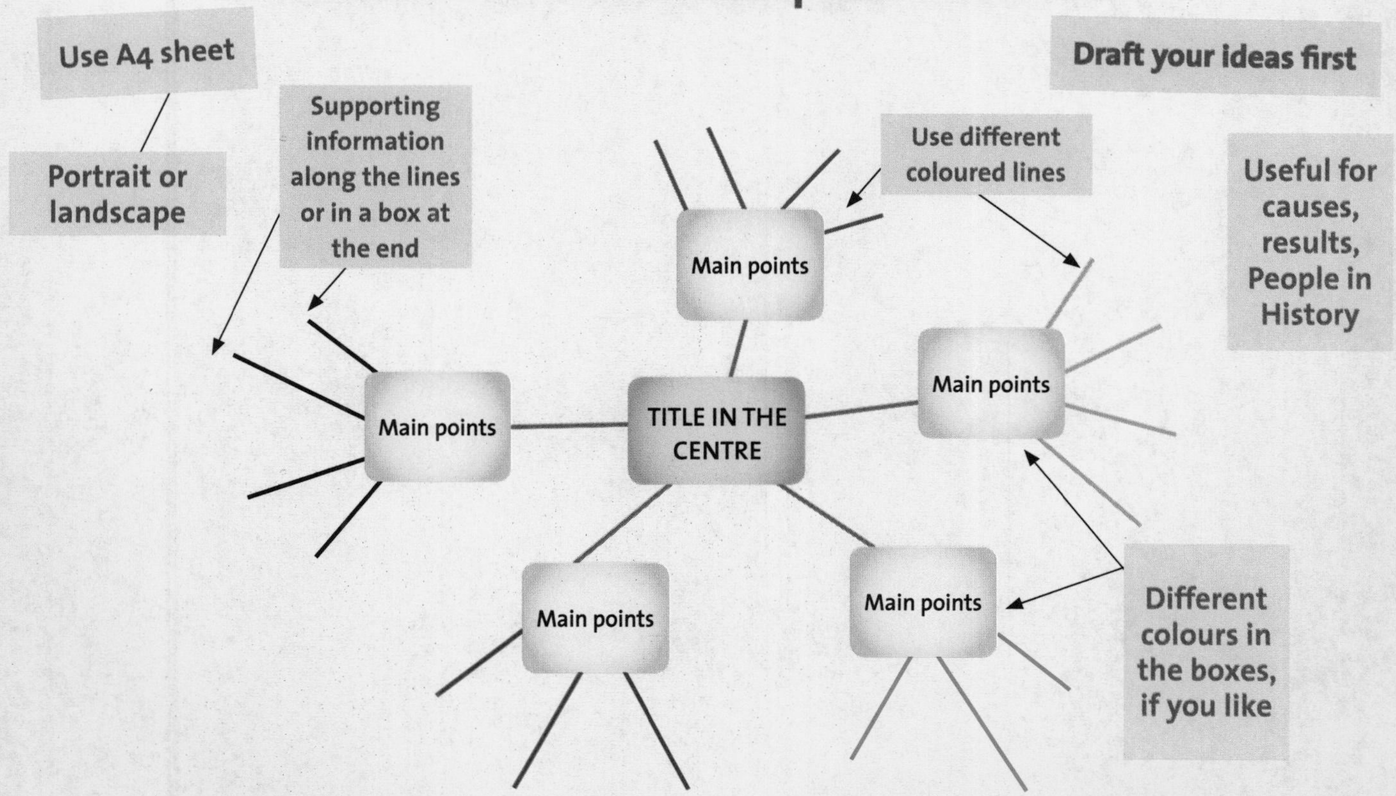

Acknowledgements

For permission to reproduce photographs, the author and publisher gratefully acknowledge the following:

Alamy: 2(E), 4(A), 4(B), 4(C), 4(D), 4(E), 12(D), 17(A), 17(C), 17(D), 18(B), 18(C), 18(F), 18(G), 18(I), 20(D), 20(E), 20(F), 25(3), 25(4), 25(5), 25(6), 26(C), 26(E), 29(A), 26(G), 47(C), 48(F), 48(I), 83(1), 83(2), 83(3), 83(4), 83(7), 83(9), 83(10), 97(3), 97(4), 106(1), 106(3), 106(4), 106(5), 106(6), 106(7), 106(8), 126(1), 126(2), 126(3), 126(4), 126(5), 126(6), 126(7), 126(8), 126(9), 126(10) • The Bridgeman Art Library: The Port of Seville, c.1590 (oil on canvas) (detail), Sanchez Coello, Alonso (1531–1589)/ Museo de America, Madrid, Spain/Bridgeman Images iiiB, 42, 50, 57, 61, 64, 66, 70, 73, 76; James Connolly (1868-1916) photographed by Lafayette, Dublin, c.1910 (sepia photo)/Private Collection/ Bridgeman Images 83(5), Countess Constance Markievicz, 1904 (b/w photo), English Photographer, (20th century)/Private Collection/Bridgeman Images 83(6) • © Central Statistics Office: 108BL, 108BC • CORBIS: 97(1), 97(5) • Getty Images: 2(G), 97(2), 97(6), 97(7) • © National Archives of Ireland: 2(F), 26(A) • © National Museum of Ireland: 17(E), 25(2) • © National Museum of Northern Ireland: 2(D) • © The National Archives Image Library (UK): iv, 81, 88, 101, 108, 117, 135, 137, 138 • By permission of the Royal Irish Academy © RIA: 25(1) • © RTÉ Stills Library: 83(8) • © Top Photo: 106(2) • © UCC/Clíodhna Ní Mhurchú: 26(1)

For permission to reproduce text, the author and publisher gratefully acknowledge the following:

© The Irish Times: page 10 • © Reprinted with permission of K. Kris Hirst: page 12 • © Kilkenny People: page 19 • © Dublinia/The Medieval Trust: page 24, page 36 • © Irish Examiner: page 27 • © Reprinted with permission of James Swan: page 53

The author and publisher have made every effort to trace all copyright holders, but if any has been inadvertently overlooked we would be pleased to make the necessary arrangement at the first opportunity.